MAT

FOR PRACTICE

Ashish Mandavia
4 Burnside Close
Twickenham
Middlesex TW1 1ET
Tel: 0181 891 0495

4

AVERAGE

SETS

OTHER BASES

ANGLES

SPEED

PETER ROBSON

PO BOX 40, SCARBOROUGH
NORTH YORKSHIRE, YO12 5TW
TEL/FAX 01723 362713

A

AVERAGE

The AVERAGE or MEAN of a set of numbers (or quantities) is the SUM (total) of all the numbers, divided by how many numbers there are.

$$\text{Average} = \frac{\text{Sum of quantities}}{\text{Number of quantities}}$$

e.g. (1) Find the average of 9, 3, 8, 4 and 11.

$$\text{Average} = \frac{9+3+8+4+11}{5} = \frac{35}{5} = 7$$

(2) Find the mean of £2.74, £3.27, £2.92, £3.03.

$$\text{Mean} = \frac{2.74+3.27+2.92+3.03}{4} = \frac{11.96}{4} = £2.99$$

REMEMBER 0 is counted as a number.

e.g. The average of 9, 7, 0, 5, 0, 3

$$= \frac{9+7+0+5+0+3}{6} = \frac{24}{6} = 4$$

Finding a missing quantity

Sum of quantities = Average X Number of quantities

e.g. The average of eight numbers is 12. Seven of the numbers are 13, 7, 18, 11, 3, 10 and 20. What is the missing number?

Sum of quantities = 12 x 8 = 96

Other seven numbers add up to
13 + 7 + 18 + 11 + 3 + 10 + 20 = 82
so missing number is 96 − 82 = 14

e.g.(2) The average mass of three samples of metal is 49 g. If one sample has mass 58 g and another has mass 37 g, what is the mass of the third sample?
Sum of quantities = 3 x 49 g = 147 g

Other two samples have mass 58 + 37 = 95 g

so mass of third sample = 147 − 95 = 52 g.

a

Find the average of each of these sets of numbers

1) 8,6,9,5

2) 36,43,38

3) 7,9,8,4,0,9,7,3,5,8

4) 117,123,121,113,131,127

5) 5.3, 6.8, 7.1, 6.4, 5.9

6) 18.55, 16.37

7) 374,389,363,328,388,350,391

8) 2.08, 1.73, 0, 3.4, 1.09

9) 9,7,4,1,1,3,8,7

10) 1276, 1253, 1315, 1292, 1308, 1254.

---

b

Find the average of each of these sets of numbers

1) £6,£12,£9,£13,£15,£4,£11

2) 80,78,56,92,67,74

3) 5.3kg,3.6kg,6.1kg,4.8kg,7.7kg

4) 41,48,42,38,45,42,50,37,44

5) 82cm, 85cm, 89cm, 94cm

6) 0,14,22,0,16,2,23,11

7) 1.9km, 3.4km, 2.3km, 3.2km

8) 5,8,9,13,12,6,10,4,7,11,14

9) £2.84, £3.18, £1.45

10) $\frac{1}{6}, \frac{2}{3}, \frac{3}{4}, \frac{7}{12}, \frac{1}{3}$

---

c

Find the values of A, B, C, D and E

1) The average of 10, 5, 12, 6, A and 14 is 9

2) The mean of 128, B, 145 and 138 is 132

3) The average of 7, 0, 27, 5, C, 18 and 11 is 13

4) The average of 48, D, 61 and 52 is 53

5) The mean of 6.46, 6.55 and E is 6.66

---

d

1) The heights of five boys were 147cm, 142cm, 137cm, 123cm, and 116cm. What was their average height?

2) Sarah bought 2 cakes at 16p each and 4 cakes at 13p each. What was the average price of a cake?

3) The hours of sunshine (to the nearest half hour) for each day in a certain week were Sunday 6½ h, Monday 3 h, Tuesday 0 h, Wednesday 9½ h, Thursday 7½ h, Friday 5 h, Saturday 10½ h. What was the daily average of hours of sunshine?

4) The heights above sea level of three hilltops are 693m, 724m and 737m. Find their mean height.

5) The average thickness of nine books is 14mm. The thicknesses of eight of the books are 8mm, 9mm, 10mm, 12mm, 16mm, 16mm, 19mm and 21mm. Find the thickness of the other book.

CLOCKS AND CALENDARS (1)

a.m. and p.m.

a.m. is short for Latin 'ante meridiem', meaning 'before noon' (before 12.00 mid-day)
p.m. is short for Latin 'post meridiem', meaning 'after noon' (after 12.00 mid-day)

e.g.	7.15 a.m.	means	7.15 in the morning
	8.40 p.m.	means	8.40 in the evening

24 HOUR CLOCK

To prevent confusion between a.m. and p.m., 24 hour clock is often used, especially in timetables for buses, trains, airlines, etc. The 24 hour clock begins at midnight (0000) and ends at the next mid-night (2400)

To write times before 1.00 p.m. in 24 hour clock, put the same times but make sure there are always four figures

e.g.	3.15 a.m.	=	0315
	9.50 a.m.	=	0950
	11.08 a.m.	=	1108
	12.47 p.m.	=	1247

To write times from 1.00 p.m. onwards in 24 hour clock, ADD 12 TO THE HOURS

e.g.	1.00 p.m.	=	13 00	1 + **12**
	5.45 p.m.	=	17 45	5 + **12**
	10.26 p.m.	=	22 26	10 + **12**

MIDNIGHT can be written either 0000 or 2400
MIDDAY (NOON) is written 1200

Note Times from 12.01 to 12.59 **a.m.** are written 0001 to 0059
Times from 12.01 to 12.59 **p.m.** are written 1201 to 1259

To convert 24 hour clock times, 1300 onwards, into p.m. times, SUBTRACT 12 FROM THE HOURS

e.g.	2355	=	11.55 p.m.	23 — **12**
	1410	=	2.10 p.m.	14 — **12**
	2000	=	8.00 p.m.	20 — **12**

REMEMBER All times after 12.00 noon (1200) are p.m.

a

Write in 24 hour clock notation

1) 6.45 a.m.	*6)* 4.13 p.m.	*11)* 3.34 a.m.
2) 11.20 a.m.	*7)* 12.00 noon	*12)* 9.05 p.m.
3) 1.35 p.m.	*8)* 9.53 a.m.	*13)* 10.17 a.m.
4) 2.00 a.m.	*9)* 2.10 p.m.	*14)* 6.58 p.m.
5) 8.32 p.m.	*10)* 10.45 p.m.	*15)* 11.11 p.m.

---

b

Write in 24 hour clock notation

1) 8.00 a.m.	*6)* 9.30 p.m.	*11)* 5.55 p.m.
2) 3.15 p.m.	*7)* 5.49 a.m.	*12)* 10.37 p.m.
3) 7.27 p.m.	*8)* 4.02 p.m.	*13)* 1.12 a.m.
4) 12.40 p.m.	*9)* 12.25 a.m.	*14)* 6.46 p.m.
5) 4.51 a.m.	*10)* 3.50 a.m.	*15)* 11.22 p.m.

---

c

Write in a.m. or p.m. notation

1) 0430	*6)* 2020	*11)* 1432
2) 1911	*7)* 1316	*12)* 1025
3) 1540	*8)* 0044	*13)* 1709
4) 0756	*9)* 1227	*14)* 0848
5) 1105	*10)* 2250	*15)* 2351

---

d

1) Copy this (imaginary) bus timetable, writing all the times in 24 hour clock.

		a.m.	p.m.	p.m.	p.m.
Orbrook	depart	9.45	2.15	3.45	7.30
Beck Edge	depart	9.55	2.25	3.55	7.40
Norford	depart	10.01	2.31	4.01	7.46
Russet Colbury	depart	10.09	2.39	4.09	7.54
Brackenhurst	depart	10.16	2.46	4.16	8.01
Tiddingfield	depart	10.23	2.53	4.23	8.08
Great Gorton	depart	10.34	3.04	4.34	8.19
Walby	arrive	10.40	3.10	4.40	8.25

2) Another bus sets off (departs) from Orbrook at 10.20 p.m. and takes exactly the same times as the other buses. Write out the full timetable for this bus, starting Orbrook depart 2220.

CLOCKS AND CALENDARS (2)

A Hours and minutes

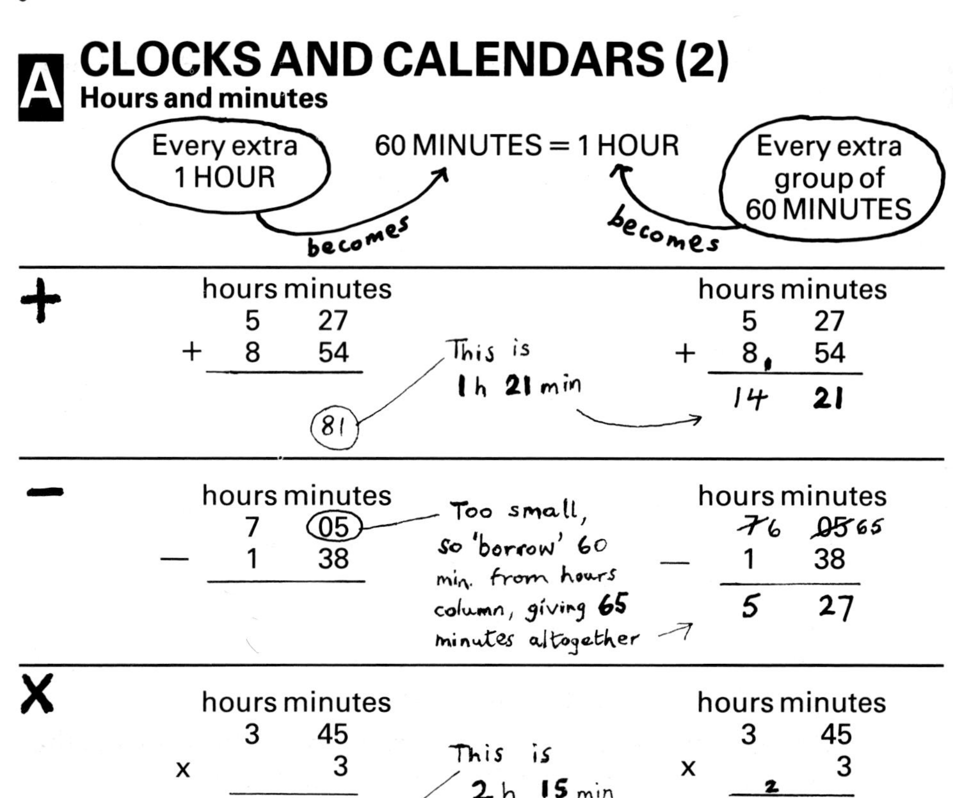

B Problems

e.g. (1) A ship set off at 0950 and travelled for 7 hours 45 minutes. At what time did it complete its journey?

	hours	minutes
	09	50
+	7	45
	17	35 (95)

It completed its journey at 1735

e.g. (2) A helicopter made 5 journeys which took a total time of 8 h 30 min. If all the journeys took the same amount of time, how long did each journey take?

$$5\,\overline{)\,8\text{ h}\quad 30\text{ min}}$$

(30 min → 210; answer: 1 h 42 min)

Each journey took 1 h 42 min

a

1)

	hours	minutes
	7	43
+	2	51

2)

	hours	minutes
	14	27
+	6	49

3)

	hours	minutes
	1	25
x		4

4)

	hours	minutes
	4	55
+	3	26

5)

	hours	minutes
	8	06
—	1	24

6)

	hours	minutes
	2	39
	1	54
+	3	47

7)

	hours	minutes
	3	38
x		5

8)

	hours	minutes
	13	12
—	7	47

9) 5) 16 h 15 min

10) 3) 8 h 15 min

---

b

1) A bus sets off on a journey at 1135 and travels for 2 hours 41 minutes At what time does it complete its journey?

2) If each lesson lasts 35 minutes, how long, in hours and minutes, do 8 lessons last?

3) Some cricketers started a match at 1030 and finished it at 1512. How long did the match last?

4) On a car journey of 10 hours 20 minutes, 4 people shared the driving equally. For how long did each person drive?

5) The four pieces of music in a concert lasted 8 minutes, 26 minutes, 15 minutes and 46 minutes. How long, in hours and minutes, did the music last altogether?

6) After travelling for 6 hours 27 minutes, a train ended its journey at 2203. At what time did it begin its journey?

7) An airliner takes 2 h 37 min to do a certain journey. Find how long 5 journeys of this length would take.

8) A satellite took 22 h 38 min to go round the Earth 7 times. How long did it take to go round once?

9) John had 4 hours of free time. He divided the time equally between playing football, writing a story and planning a new hutch for his rabbit. How much time, in hours and minutes, did he spend on each activity?

10) Each day a village shop opens at 0815 and closes at 1300 for lunch. Then it opens again at 1400 and closes at 1900. (a) For how long is it open each day? (b) If it opens every day of the week, including Sunday, for how long is it open each week?

CLOCKS AND CALENDARS (3)

Going past midnight

When adding a time from one day to the next, SUBTRACT 24 HOURS from your answer.

e.g. A ship left Liverpool at 2215 and took 8 h 50 min to reach Dublin. At what time did the ship arrive in Dublin?

	h	min
	22	15
+	8	50
	31	05

	h	min
	31	05
−	24	00
	07	05

The ship arrived in Dublin at 0705 the next day

When subtracting a time from one day to the previous day (the day before) 'BORROW' 24 HOURS before you start.

e.g. A train set off from Newcastle at 1950 on Friday and reached Plymouth at 0456 on Saturday. How long did its journey take?

	h	min
	04	56
−	19	50

+ 24 HOURS =

	h	min
	28	56
−	19	50
	9	06

The train took 9 hours 6 minutes

Average times

$$\text{Average} = \frac{\text{Sum of quantities}}{\text{Number of quantities}}$$

e.g. A train's arrival times on the days of a certain week were 2006, 1955, 2002, 1954, 1953, 1958, 2005. What was its average time of arrival?

	h	min
	20	06
	19	55
	20	02
	19	54
	19	53
	19	58
+	20	05
	139	53 (233)

	h	min
	19	59
7)	139 rem. 6	~~53~~ 413

Average time of arrival of train was 19 59

a

1) Martin went to sleep at 2237 and slept for 8 hours 47 minutes. At what time did he wake up?

2) On a certain evening the sun set at 1944 and rose the next morning at 0407. Calculate the length of time between sunset and sunrise.

3) A train left Stirling at 2223 and arrived in London 7 hours 39 minutes later. At what time did it arrive in London?

4) A night porter at a hotel began work at 2315 and finished work at 0500 the next morning. How long did he work?

5) An airliner left London at 2045 and travelled to Accra, arriving there at 0336 the next day. How long did its journey take?

6) Aunt Lucy set off from Liverpool at 1950 and drove to Southampton. The journey took 7 h 27 min. At what time did she reach Southampton?

7) A shop opens from 0715 until 2030 each day. How long is it from closing time each evening until opening time the next morning?

8) A group of long-distance walkers started a walk on Saturday evening. Their walk took them 11 hours 35 minutes and they finished it at 0920 on Sunday morning. At what time did they start?

9) David set off on a journey at 1425 on Wednesday and reached the end of his journey at 1150 on Friday. How long, in hours and minutes, did the journey take?

10) A swimming pool began to be filled with water at 1840 on Monday evening. The pool took 26 h 35 min to fill. At what time on which day was the pool full?

---

b

1) Find the average of 6 h 37 min, 5 h 42 min and 6 h 29 min.

2) Find the average of 3 h 14 min, 2 h 48 min, 1 h 57 min, 2 h 22 min, 1 h 54 min.

3) On six days of a certain week a train arrived in Bristol at 1540, 1549, 1545, 1543, 1548 and 1539. (a) What was its average time of arrival? (b) If it should have arrived at 1545 each day, how many minutes early or late was it on average?

4) What is the average of 5 h 8 min, 4 h 39 min, 5 h 26 min, 4 h 15 min?

5) School began at 0855. One week Peter arrived at school at 0841, 0852, 0846, 0838 and 0843. Find out the daily average number of minutes he was early for school.

A CLOCKS AND CALENDARS (4)

Years and months

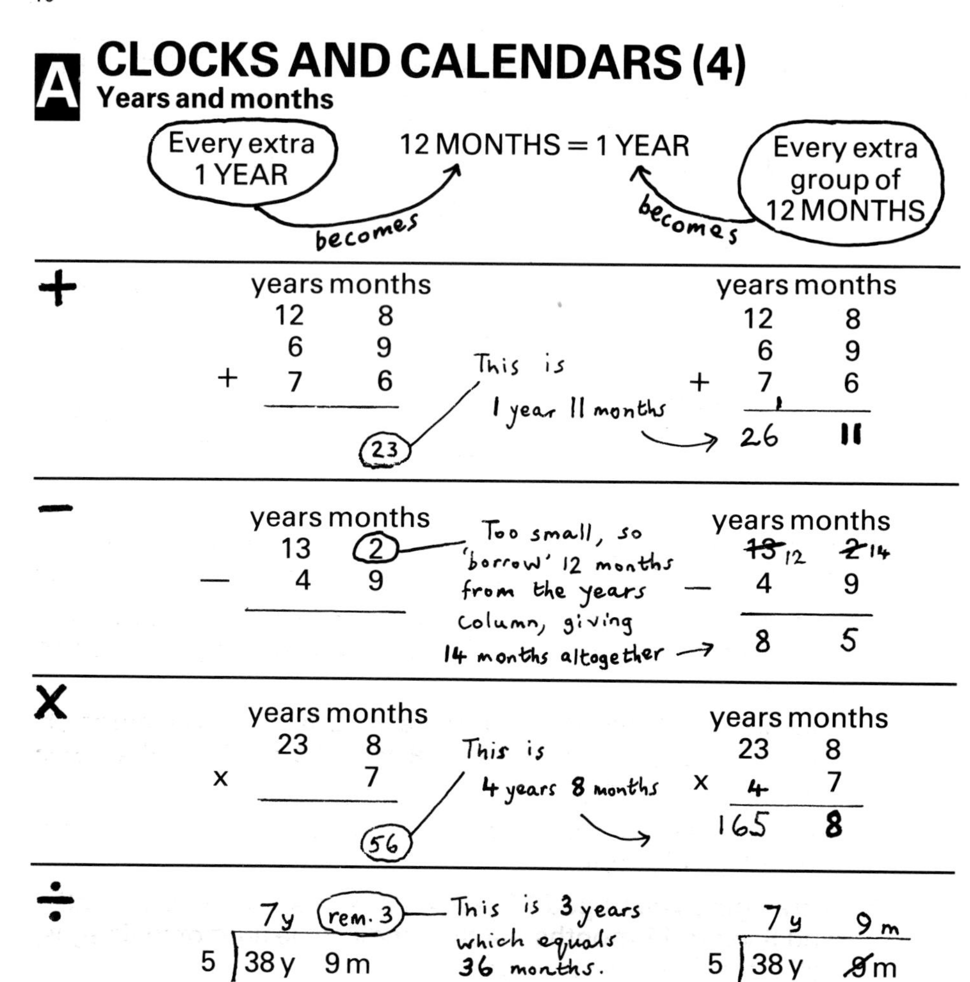

Months of the year

1. January
2. February
3. March
4. April
5. May
6. June
7. July
8. August
9. September
10. October
11. November
12. December

e.g. Amy was born in May 1982. Thomas was born 2 years 8 months before Amy. When was Thomas born?

	years	months
	~~1982~~ 1981	~~5~~ 17
−	2	8
	1979	9

Thomas was born in September 1979

a

1) years months

	years	months
	5	6
	4	2
+	3	11

2) years months

	years	months
	7	9
x		3

3) years months

	years	months
	24	2
—	18	9

4) years months

	years	months
	13	8
x		5

5) 3) 17 y 6 m

6) years months

	years	months
	36	10
	37	10
+	33	3

7) 7) 25 y 1 m

8) years months

	years	months
	5	0
—	1	10

9) years months

	years	months
	19	3
x		4

10) years months

	years	months
	45	1
—	27	5

b

1) Sally's three dogs are aged 5 years 7 months, 3 years 4 months and 1 year 9 months. What is the sum of their ages?

2) Simon was born in August 1977. His brother Lee was born 3 years 9 months later. In which month of which year was Lee born?

3) The battle of Waterloo took place in June 1815. The battle of Trafalgar was fought 9 years 8 months earlier. When was the battle of Trafalgar?

4) Bill is 8 years 11 months old. His father is 4 times Bill's age. How old is his father?

5) Three girls were aged 13 years 4 months, 11 years 0 months and 9 years 11 months. By first finding the sum of their ages, calculate their average age.

6) Mr. Green's car was new in January 1987; Mr. Brown's car was new in May 1979. In years and months, how much older than Mr. Green's car is Mr. Brown's car?

7) Ian was born in March 1986. His cousin Andrew was born 7 years 4 months before Ian. When was Andrew born?

8) Lisa's age is 5 times the age of her youngest brother. Lisa is 14 years 7 months old. How old is her youngest brother?

9) King Edward I of England reigned from November 1272 until July 1307. How long, in years and months, did he reign?

10) Jim is 9 years 9 months old, Tom is 11 years 3 months old, George is 9 years 10 months old and Peter is 10 years 6 months old. Find (a) the sum of their ages, (b) their average age.

SETS (1)

A

A set is a group or collection of things.
Each thing in a set is called a MEMBER or ELEMENT.

The set of can be written { }

e.g. 'the set of days of the week' can be written
{days of the week}
'the set of wild animals' can be written
{wild animals}

A set can also be written out in full to show all its MEMBERS,
e.g. 'the set of seasons' can be written {winter, autumn, spring, summer}

Members of a set may be written in any order.

B

$\in$ means 'is a member of'
e.g. autumn is a member of the set of seasons can be written
autumn $\in$ {seasons}
blue is a member of the set of colours can be written
blue $\in$ {colours}

$\notin$ means 'is NOT a member of'
e.g. sheepdog is not a member of the set of prime numbers
sheepdog $\notin$ {prime numbers}

C

Sets are often given a capital letter name to identify them, e.g.
A = {animals}
P = {prime numbers}
T = {pupils in Form 3} , etc.

D

How to draw the brackets for sets
For the beginning of the set, draw a very thin S with a very thin backwards S underneath. For the end of the set, draw them the other way round. { }

a

Write, using brackets

e.g. The set of trees = {trees}

1) The set of seasons
2) The set of triangles
3) The set of spaceships
4) The set of tortoises
5) The set of books
6) The set of puddings
7) The set of ghosts
8) The set of sailing boats
9) The set of birds
10) The set of pyramids

---

b

Write, using letters and brackets

e.g. Set A is the set of alligators A = {alligators}

1) Set C is the set of African countries
2) Set Z is the set of footballs
3) Set H is the set of hamsters
4) Set S is the set of sausages
5) Set F is the set of flowers

---

c

Write, using signs $\in$, $\notin$ and brackets

e.g. Venus is a member of the set of planets

Venus $\in$ {planets}

1) N is a member of the set of letters
2) Charles is a member of the set of boys' names
3) sugar is not a member of the set of animals
4) 23 is a member of the set of prime numbers
5) Finland is not a member of the set of colours
6) tennis is not a member of the set of English kings
7) oxygen is a member of the set of elements
8) oak is a member of the set of trees
9) * is not a member of the set of ponies
10) apple pie is a member of the set of pies

SETS (2)

Venn diagrams

A Venn diagram is a way of showing sets in picture form. Each set is drawn as a rough circle, ring or egg shape.

e.g. Set A as a Venn diagram would be drawn

e.g. Set F = {cod, haddock, plaice} would be drawn

The space inside a Venn diagram is called a REGION.
Venn diagrams were named after their inventor, the Reverend John Venn (born 1834, died 1923).

Empty set

An empty set is a set which contains no members. It is also called a NULL set or a VOID set. It can be written either $\emptyset$ or { }

e.g. If set S is the set of four-cornered triangles

$$S = \emptyset \quad \textbf{or} \quad S = \{\ \}$$

If G is the set of giraffes fitted with diesel engines

$$G = \emptyset \quad \textbf{or} \quad G = \{\ \}$$

Number of members of a set is written n followed by the name of the set in ordinary brackets

e.g. If set V = {A, E, I, O, U} the number of members in the set is 5, so

$$n(V) = 5$$

If set W = {Monday, Tuesday, Wednesday, Thursday, Friday, Saturday, Sunday}

$$n(W) = 7$$

If set D = {3}

$$n(D) = 1$$

The number of members of an empty set is 0

e.g. If set J = $\emptyset$, n (J) = 0

a

Draw a Venn diagram to show each of these sets

1) Set B = {John, Michael, Roger}
2) Set P = {2, 3, 5, 7, 11, 13, 17, 19}
3) Set L = {London, Lisbon, Leeds, Los Angeles, Liverpool}
4) Set J = ϕ
5) Set D = {N, E, S, W}
6) Set S = {21, 36, 55, 60, 67, 68, 92, 93, 125}
7) Set V = {carrot, onion}
8) Set Y = { }
9) Set O = {Pacific, Atlantic, Indian, Arctic}
10) Set E = {+, —, ×, ÷}

---

b

For each of the sets in part **a** (the questions at the top of the page), copy and complete the following to show the number of members of each set

1) n(B) =
2) n(P) =
3) n(L) =
4) n(J) =
5) n(D) =
6) n(S) =
7) n(V) =
8) n(Y) =
9) n(O) =
10) n(E) =

---

c

List the members of each of these sets, e.g.
W. The set of days of the week.
W = {Sunday, Monday, Tuesday, Wednesday, Thursday, Friday, Saturday}
If there are no members, write ϕ

1) A. The set of odd numbers between 0 and 10
2) B. The set of seasons of the year
3) C. The set of five-sided triangles
4) D. The set of names of months beginning with the letter J
5) E. The set of integers greater than $^-6$ but less than $^-1$
6) F. The set of prime numbers between 20 and 30
7) G. The set of jellies that can ride bicycles
8) H. The set of letters of the alphabet after g but before n
9) I. The set of invisible things which can be seen
10) J. The set of multiples of 6 which are less than 25

A SETS (3)
SUBSETS

A SUBSET is a set which is a small part of another set
e.g. {maths teachers} is a subset of {teachers}
{alarm clocks} is a subset of {clocks}
{6, 7, 8} is a subset of {5, 6, 7, 8, 9, 10}
The sign $\subset$ means 'is a SUBSET of'
e.g. {green cars} $\subset$ {cars}
{B, C} $\subset$ {A, B, C}

B Listing all the subsets of a set

e.g. (1) The subsets of {apple, banana} are
{apple, banana}, {apple}, {banana}, $\emptyset$
e.g. (2) The subsets of {1, 3, 5} are
{1, 3, 5}, {1, 3}, {1, 5}, {3, 5}, {1}, {3}, {5}, $\emptyset$

<u>REMEMBER</u> (1) A set is a subset of itself
e.g. {horses} $\subset$ {horses}
(2) An empty set is a subset of any other set
e.g. $\emptyset \subset$ {A, E, I, O, U}
(3) Members of a set may be written in any order
e.g. {1, 5} is the same set as {5, 1}

Venn diagram of a subset is drawn as a smaller ring inside a larger ring
e.g. D = {ducks}
N = {noisy ducks}

N $\subset$ D

e.g. F = {1, 2, 3, 4, 5, 6, 7}
P = {2, 3, 5, 7}

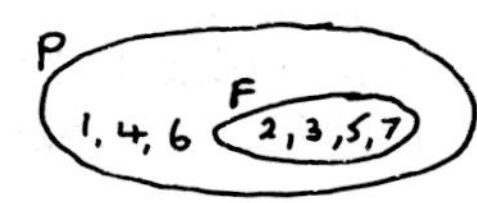

F $\subset$ P

NOTE. In a Venn diagram, each member may be written
ONLY ONCE

D Contains as a subset

$\supset$ means 'contains as a subset'
e.g. If {British mountains} $\subset$ {mountains}
then {mountains} $\supset$ {British mountains}
$\not\subset$ means 'is NOT a subset of'
$\not\supset$ means 'does NOT contain as a subset'

a

Write in short, using $\subset$
e.g. A is a subset of B $\quad A \subset B$

1) {brick walls} is a subset of {walls}
2) {Scotsmen} is a subset of {men}
3) Q is a subset of P
4) {fizzy drinks} is a subset of {drinks}
5) {B, C, D} is a subset of {A, B, C, D, E}

---

b

Write in short, using $\subset$, $\not\subset$, $\in$, $\notin$, $\emptyset$, { }

1) {frying pan} is not a subset of {animals}
2) violin is a member of the set of instruments
3) G is an empty set
4) lollipop is not a member of the set of gorillas
5) {3, 5, 7} is a subset of {1, 3, 5, 7, 9, 11}

---

c

Make a list of all the subsets of each set

1) {cabbage, turnip}
2) {Emma, Kate, Tina}
3) {1, 2, 3, 4}
4) {red, blue, green}
5) {P, Q, R, S, T}

---

d

Draw a Venn diagram to show each of the following.
Put each member in its correct region

1) {24, 36} is a subset of {12, 24, 36, 48, 60}
2) {pine, larch} is a subset of {oak, pine, beech, larch}
3) {f, g, h} is a subset of {a, b, c, d, e, f, g, h}
4) {deuce} is a subset of {love, 15, 30, 40, advantage, deuce}
5) {9, 10, 11, 12} is a subset of {9, 10, 11, 12, 13}

---

e

For each of these pairs of sets, draw a Venn diagram showing the subset inside the larger set. Remember that each member may be written only once

1) {cricket, tennis}; {cricket, hockey, netball, tennis}
2) {P, Q, R, S, T}; {P, R, T}
3) {wasp, bee, hornet};
   {butterfly, bee, wasp, dragonfly, hornet, ladybird}
4) {yellow, green, red, blue}; {red}
5) {5, 6, 7, 8, 9}; {7, 8}

A SETS (4)

Intersection ('CAP')

Two (or more) different sets may have one or more members in common. The shared set which contains these members is called the INTERSECTION of the original sets.

Intersection is written $\cap$ and often called CAP

e.g. Set L = {a, b, c, d, e, f}
Set V = {a, e, i, o, u}

The members a and e are members of **both sets** so {a, e} is the intersection of sets L and V (L cap V).

Set L $\cap$ V = {a, e}

B

In a Venn diagram, intersection is shown by overlapping

e.g. L = {a, b, c, d, e, f}
V = {a, e, i, o, u}
L $\cap$ V = {a, e}

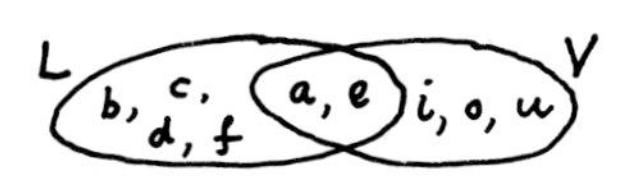

The region in the middle is the set L $\cap$ V, the intersection of sets L and V

---

e.g (2)
J = {James, John, Joseph, Jennifer}
G = {Christine, Jennifer, Sara}
J $\cap$ G = {Jennifer}

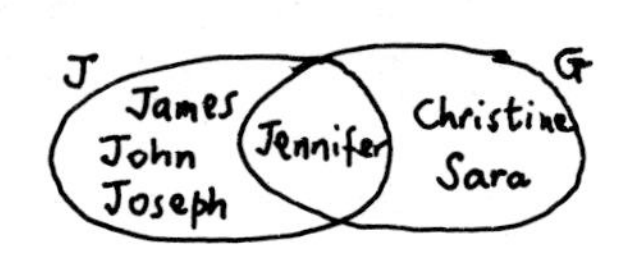

---

e.g. (3)
A = {h, j, k, o, v}
B = {h, k, o, p, t}
C = {g, k, p, q, t, v}
A $\cap$ B = {h, o, k}
A $\cap$ C = {v, k}
B $\cap$ C = {p, t, k}

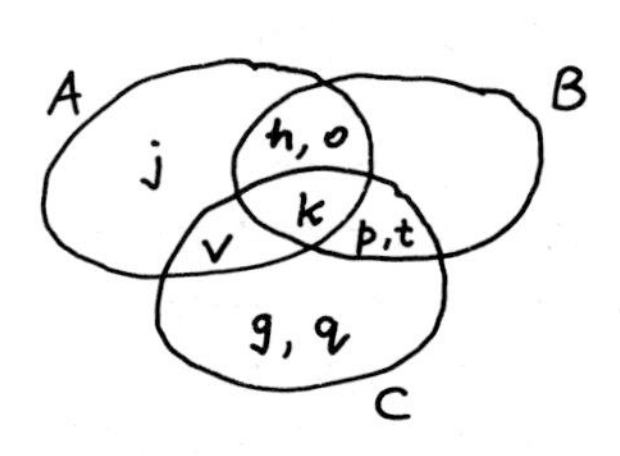

The very middle region is called A $\cap$ B $\cap$ C

A $\cap$ B $\cap$ C = {k}

a

Find the intersection of each of these pairs of sets
e.g. A = {1, 2, 3}, B = {2, 3, 5, 7}. **Answer** A ∩ B = {2, 3}

1) C = {k, m, n, p, q, r}, D = {j, k, p, r, s, t}
2) E = {5, 10, 15, 20, 25}, F = {10, 20, 30, 40, 50}
3) G = {Matthew, Mark, Luke, John}, H = {Carl, Peter, James}
4) J = $\{\frac{5}{4}, \frac{8}{3}, \frac{16}{15}, \frac{9}{4}, \frac{11}{6}, \frac{11}{4}, \frac{7}{4}\}$, K = $\{\frac{1}{4}, \frac{3}{4}, \frac{5}{4}, \frac{7}{4}, \frac{9}{4}, \frac{11}{4}\}$
5) L = { ⚅ ⚄ ⚁ ⚃ }, M = { ⚀ ⚁ ⚂ }

---

b

Draw a larger copy of the Venn diagram to show each pair of sets. Write each member in its correct region

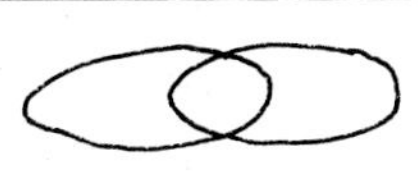

1) Z = {%, ≏, <, ÷}, Y = {✓, %, +}
2) A = {4, 8, 12, 16, 20}, S = {1, 4, 9, 16, 25}
3) H = {Britten, Bach, Bizet}, J = {Beethoven, Bruch, Bach}
4) U = {f, g, h, i, j, k,}, V = {g, h, i, j, k, l, m}
5) C = {4, 5, 6, 7, 8}, E = {2, 4, 6, 8}

---

c

Draw a larger copy of the Venn diagram to show each group of sets. Write each member in its correct region

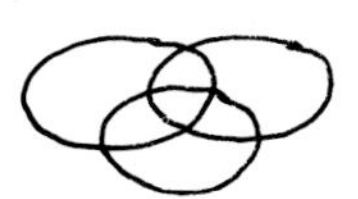

1) A = {2, 4, 6, 8, 10}, B = {1, 2, 3, 4}, C = {4, 8, 12, 16}
2) P = {a,b,c,e,h,j,k}, Q = {e,f,g,h,j,k,m}
R = {c,d,e,f,g,}
3) W = {■, ▽, ★, ◇}, X = {★, O, ◇, ◆},
Y = {☆, ◇, ●, ◆, ★}
4) J = {2, 3, 5, 7}, K = {2, 3, 4, 6}, L = {3, 5, 6, 8}
5) F = {Dan, Jim, Joe, Sam}, M = {Ben, Dan, Pat, Tom},
T = {Ben, Bob, Dan, Joe, Tom}

---

d

For each of these groups of sets, draw the best possible Venn diagram and write each member in its correct region

1) C = {x, y, z}, D = {v, w, x, y, z}
2) R = {19, 23, 29, 31, 37}, T = {31, 37, 41, 43}
3) K = { λ , ᛚ , ⊦ , ⊣ }, M = { ⅄ , ᛚ , ᛕ }
4) F = {2½, 5½, 6½, 7½, 9½}, P = {5½}
5) B = {p, s, t, w, y}, E = {q, s, t, v, w, y},
G = {s, t, w, y, z}

SETS (5)

Union ('CUP')

The UNION of two (or more) sets is the **set containing all the members** of both (or all) sets.

Union is written $\cup$ and often called CUP

e.g. P = {Thames, Tay, Tees, Trent, Tweed}
Q = {Clyde, Tay, Tweed, Dee, Forth}

The union of sets P and Q is
$P \cup Q$ = {Thames, Trent, Tees, Tay, Tweed, Clyde, Dee, Forth}

NOTE Each member of the union should be listed ONLY ONCE. Do NOT repeat any members (e.g. do **not** write Tay, Tay, Tweed, Tweed)

Union of three sets is written $A \cup B \cup C$, etc.

Venn diagrams to show H.C.F. and L.C.M.

e.g. Find the H.C.F. and L.C.M. of 24 and 90 by drawing a Venn diagram

1) Express 24 and 90 as products of prime factors

2	24
2	12
2	6
3	3
	1

2	90
3	45
3	15
5	5
	1

2) Draw a Venn diagram and write down the factors

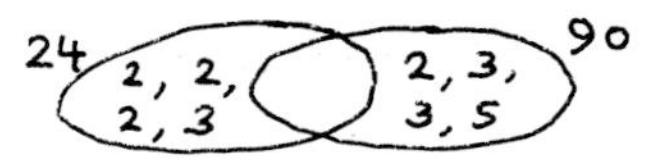

3) If any factors are **common** to both (or all) sets, write them in the intersection and rub out (or cross out) the originals

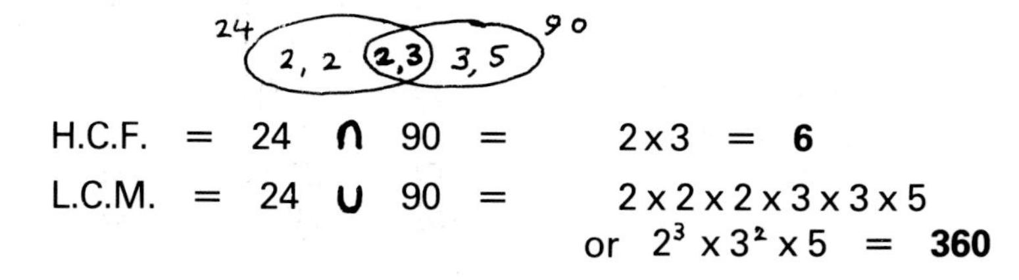

H.C.F. = $24 \cap 90$ = 2×3 = **6**

L.C.M. = $24 \cup 90$ = $2 \times 2 \times 2 \times 3 \times 3 \times 5$
or $2^3 \times 3^2 \times 5$ = **360**

a

Find the union of these pairs of sets
e.g. Y = {27, 28, 29, 30}, Z = {20, 30, 40}

Answer Y $\cup$ Z = {20, 27, 28, 29, 30, 40}

1) A = {4, 5, 6, 7}, K = {1, 2, 3, 4, 5, 6}
2) T = {red, yellow, green}, B = {blue, green, black, red}
3) Q = {a, b, c, d, e}, R = {a, b, c}
4) J = {January, June, July}, M = {July, August, September}
5) P = {2, 3, 5, 7, 11, 13}, N = {4, 8, 12, 16}

---

b

Find the intersection ($\cap$) and union ($\cup$) of each of these pairs of sets

1) B = {rook, blackbird, starling}, C = {bishop, knight, rook}
2) T = {Ω, T, Γ, Σ}, V = {Γ, ρ, Ψ, T, Ω}
3) F = {iron, zinc, copper, chromium, cadmium}
G = {carbon, cadmium, chlorine, chromium, copper}
4) N = {e, f, g, h, j}, Q = {c, d}
5) D = {9, 11}, K = {8, 9, 10, 11, 12}

---

c

Find the H.C.F. and L.C.M. of each group of numbers. Draw a Venn diagram of each answer

1) 120, 45
2) 84, 154
3) 96, 48
4) 35, 56
5) 24, 64
6) 110, 66
7) 180, 168
8) 270, 234
9) 18, 48, 84
10) 24, 44, 60

---

d

Look at the Venn diagram. Copy the questions and complete them with the correct answers

e.g. R = { } **Answer** R = {3, 6, 9, 12, 15}

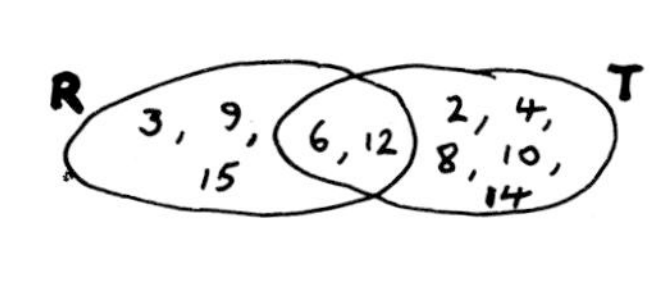

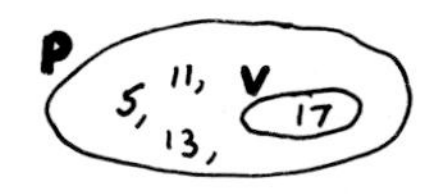

1) T = { }
2) R $\cap$ T = { }
3) n (R) =
4) P $\cup$ R = { }
5) n (P) =
6) P $\cap$ T =
7) P $\cup$ V = { }
8) V $\subset$
9) n (R $\cap$ T) =
10) V $\cap$ P = { }

SETS (6)

Disjoint sets are sets which have nothing in common. They do not share any members.

e.g. (1) A = {1, 2, 3, 4}, B = {8, 9} are DISJOINT sets

(2) S = {a, b, c}, T = {□, △, ☆} are DISJOINT sets

In a Venn diagram, disjoint sets are shown as unconnected regions, e.g.

F= {21, 22, 23}, G = {w, x, y, z}

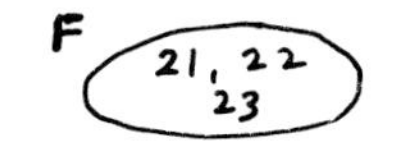

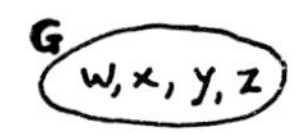

The intersection of disjoint sets is always an empty set

Universal set is the set containing **everything** you are dealing with. It is usually shown by the sign ℰ . All other sets are subsets of the universal set.

The Venn diagram of the universal set is usually drawn as a rectangle

e.g.

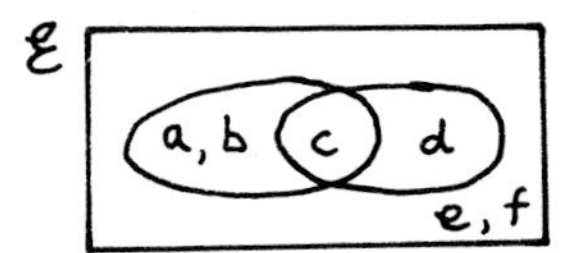

ℰ = {a, b, c, d, e, f}

'NOT' (Complement of a set)

The complement of a set contains all the members of the universal set which are not in the set.

The complement of set A is written A′

e.g.

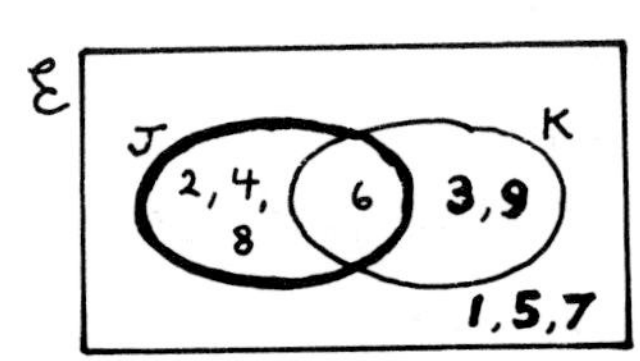

The complement of J (sometimes called **NOT J**)

J′ = {1, 3, 5, 7, 9}

a Draw a larger version of this Venn diagram to show each of these groups of sets.

1) $S = \{+, \times, \div, \neq\}$, $T = \{13, 27, 44\}$
2) G = {orange, lemon}, D = {onion, leek, carrot}
3) A = {Ford, VW, Fiat, Citroën}, L = {ш, ю, я}
4) $H = \{a, c, e, g, i\}$, $B = \{\tfrac{1}{2}, \tfrac{1}{4}, \tfrac{1}{8}\}$
5) N = {♪, ♩, 𝅗𝅥, 𝅝}, C = {Avon, Kent}

---

b Draw a larger version of this Venn diagram to show each of these groups of sets. Write members in the correct regions.

1) $\mathcal{E} = \{1, 2, 3, 4, 5, 6\}$, $A = \{3, 4, 5\}$
2) $\mathcal{E} = \{r, s, t, u, v, w, x\}$, $B = \{r, s, t, u, v, w\}$
3) $\mathcal{E} = \{12, 13, 14, 15, 16\}$, $C = \{12, 13, 14, 15, 16\}$
4) $\mathcal{E} = \{\frac{1}{5}, \frac{3}{10}, \frac{2}{5}, \frac{1}{2}\}$, $D = \{\frac{1}{2}\}$
5) $\mathcal{E} = \{I, V, X, L, C, D, M\}$, $E = \{L, D\}$

---

c From the groups of sets in part **b** on this page, find the members of

1) A'
2) B'
3) C'
4) D'
5) E'

---

d Draw a larger version of this Venn diagram to show each of these groups of sets. Write members in the correct regions. Underneath each diagram, copy and complete

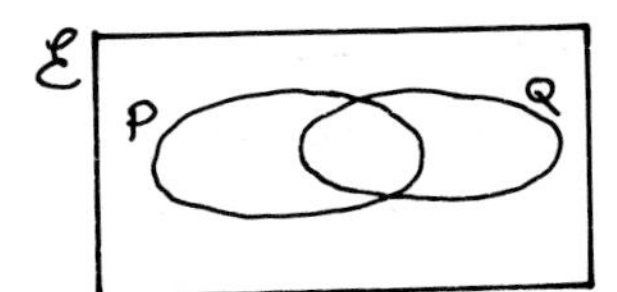

$P \cap Q =$
$Q' =$
$n(P \cup Q) =$

In all the questions $\mathcal{E} = \{1, 2, 3, 4, 5, 6, 7, 8, 9\}$

1) $P = \{1, 2, 3, 4\}$, $Q = \{3, 4, 5, 6\}$
2) $P = \{8, 9\}$, $Q = \{5, 7, 9\}$
3) $P = \{1, 2, 3\}$, $Q = \{1, 2, 3, 4, 5, 6, 7, 8, 9\}$
4) $P = \{3, 5\}$, $Q = \{4\}$
5) $P = \{3, 4, 5, 6, 7, 8, 9\}$, $Q = \{1, 3, 4, 5, 6, 7\}$

A

SETS (7)
Revision
SET SIGNS

Make sure you know what all these signs mean

$\in$	is a member of	$\mathcal{E}$	universal set
$\notin$	is not a member of	n	number of members of
$\subset$	is a subset of	$\{\quad\}$	the set of
$\cap$	intersection (CAP)	$\emptyset$	empty set
$\cup$	union (CUP)	A′	not A (complement of A)

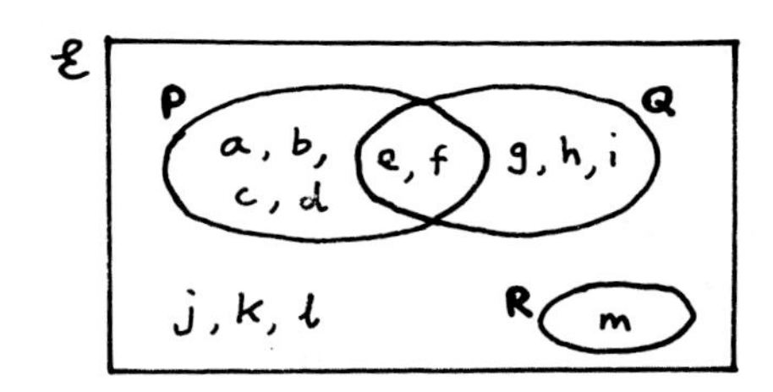

The universal set contains the sets P, Q and R

$\mathcal{E} = \{a, b, c, d, e, f, g, h, i, j, k, l, m\}$

$P = \{a, b, c, d, e, f\}$

$Q = \{e, f, g, h, i\}$

$R = \{m\}$

$P \cap Q = \{e, f\}$

$P \cap R = \emptyset$

$Q \cap R = \emptyset$

$P \cap Q \cap R = \emptyset$

$P \cup Q = \{a, b, c, d, e, f, g, h, i\}$

$P \cup R = \{a, b, c, d, e, f, m\}$

$Q \cup R = \{e, f, g, h, i, m\}$

$P \cup Q \cup R = \{a, b, c, d, e, f, g, h, i, m\}$

$P' = \{g, h, i, j, k, l, m\}$

$Q' = \{a, b, c, d, j, k, l, m\}$

$R' = \{a, b, c, d, e, f, g, h, i, j, k, l\}$

$(P \cup Q)' = \{j, k, l, m\}$

$(P \cap Q)' = \{a, b, c, d, g, h, i, j, k, l, m\}$

$(P \cup Q \cup R)' = \{j, k, l\}$

$P \cap Q' = \{a, b, c, d\}$

$P' \cap Q = \{g, h, i\}$

$n(P) = 6$

$n(Q) = 5$

$n(R) = 1$

$n(\mathcal{E}) = 13$

$n(P \cap Q) = 2$

$n(P \cup R) = 7$

$R \subset \mathcal{E}$

$c \in P$

$k \notin Q$ etc.

a Copy and complete the questions

1) $H = \{$ ....
2) $J = \{$ ....
3) $H \cap J = \{$ .....
4) $H' = \{$ ....
5) $n(J') =$ ....
6) $n(H \cup J) =$ ....
7) $H \cap J' = \{$ ....
8) $H' \cap J' = \{$ ....
9) $H' \cup J' = \{$ ....
10) $n(\mathcal{E}) = \{$ ....

$\mathcal{E}$
H J
8, 9, 5 | 4, 3, 7 | 6
1, 2

b $\mathcal{E}$

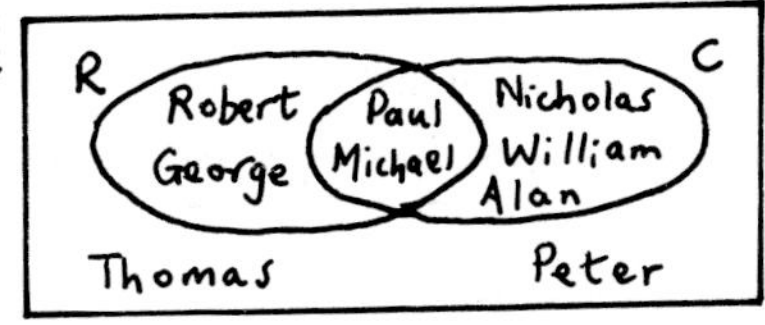

$\mathcal{E} = \{$boys in Form 3$\}$
$R = \{$Form 3 boys in the rugby team$\}$
$C = \{$Form 3 boys in the choir$\}$

List the members of these sets and describe the sets in writing
e.g. $R \cap C' = \{$George, Robert$\} = \{$Form 3 boys who are in the rugby team but not in the choir$\}$

1) $R \cap C =$
2) $R' =$
3) $R \cup C =$
4) $(R \cup C)' =$
5) $R' \cap C =$

c $\mathcal{E} = \{j, k, n, p, q, r, s, t, u, v, w, x, y, z\}$
$A = \{j, p, u, v, w\}$
$B = \{j, p, q, r, s, w\}$
$C = \{n, p, r, s, t, w, x, y\}$

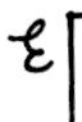

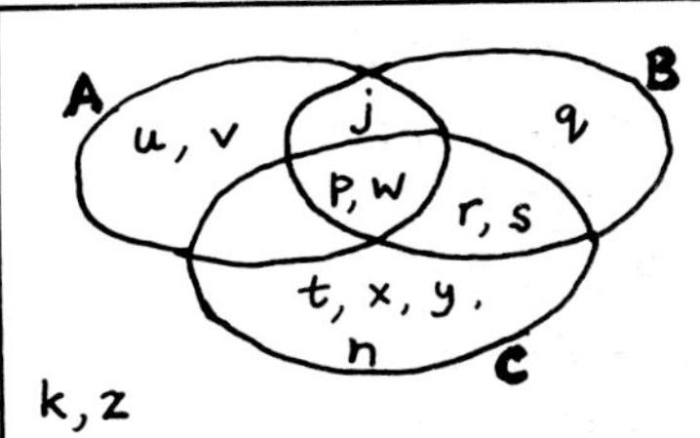

Copy and complete these questions

1) $A \cap B = \{$ ....
2) $C' = \{$ ....
3) $n(B) =$ ....
4) $A \cup B \cup C = \{$ ....
5) $A \cap B \cap C = \{$ ....
6) $\{x, y\} \subset$ ....
7) $n(A \cap C) =$ ....
8) $r \notin$ ....
9) $C \cap A' = \{$ ....
10) $n(\mathcal{E}) =$ ....
11) $A \cap B' = \{$ ....
12) $n(B') =$ ....
13) $u \in$ ....
14) $(A \cup B \cup C)' = \{$ ....
15) $A \cap C \cap B' = \{$ ....

A SETS (8) Using a Venn Diagram

e.g. Draw a Venn diagram to show the correct NUMBER OF MEMBERS in each region

18 boxes altogether (set ℰ)
5 empty boxes (set B)

Empty boxes is a subset of boxes.
There are (18 − 5) = 13 boxes which are NOT empty (set B′)
so the Venn diagram is drawn

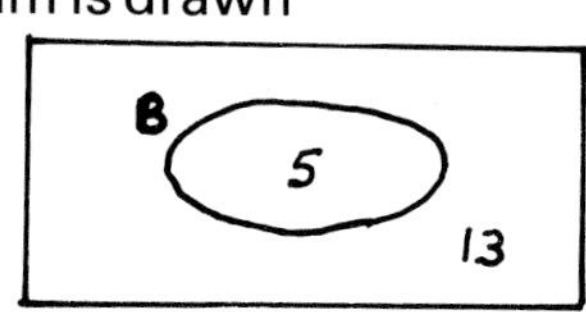

e.g. Draw a Venn diagram to show the correct NUMBER OF MEMBERS in each region

47 passengers altogether (set ℰ)
8 French passengers (set F)
6 Austrian passengers (set A)

Sets F and A are **disjoint** subsets of set ℰ. Apart from French and Austrian passengers there are (47 − 8 − 6) = 33 passengers, so the Venn diagram is drawn

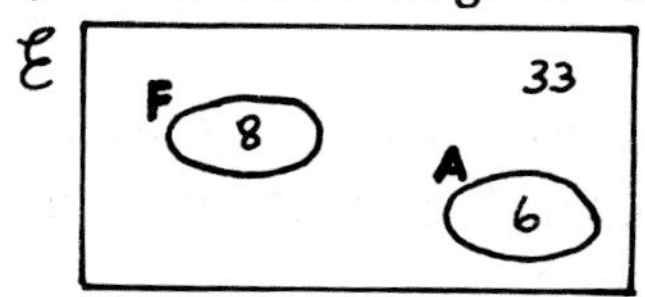

e.g. Draw a Venn diagram to show the correct NUMBER OF MEMBERS in each region

60 books altogether (set ℰ)
34 new books (set N)
19 history books (set H)
7 new history books (set $N \cap H$)

There are 7 new history books, so there are (34 − 7) = 27 new books which are not history books, and (19 − 7) = 12 history books which are not new. This leaves (60 − 7 − 27 − 12) = 14 books which are neither new books nor history books, so the Venn diagram is drawn

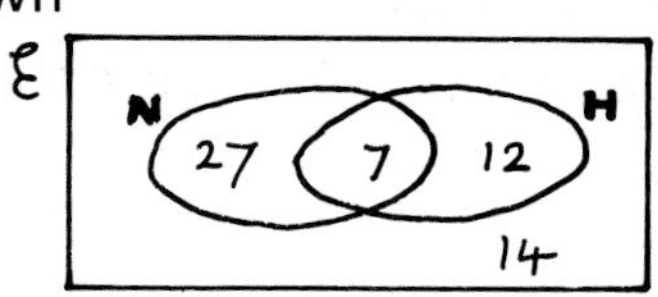

a For each pair of sets, draw a Venn diagram with the same pattern as the one on page 26 **A** Place the correct NUMBER OF MEMBERS in each region.

1) 21 sheep altogether (set $\mathcal{E}$), 6 black sheep (set B)
2) 13 trees altogether (set $\mathcal{E}$) 4 pine trees (set P)
3) 55 coins altogether (set $\mathcal{E}$), 18 gold coins (set G)
4) 12 footballs altogether (set $\mathcal{E}$), 5 leather footballs (set L)
5) 313 people altogether (set $\mathcal{E}$), 29 Welsh people (set W)

---

b For each group of sets, draw a Venn diagram with the same pattern as the one on page 26 **B**. Place the correct NUMBER OF MEMBERS in each region.

1) 25 balloons altogether (set $\mathcal{E}$), 7 green balloons (set G), 8 red balloons (set R)
2) 16 boats altogether (set $\mathcal{E}$), 8 rowing boats (set R), 5 sailing boats (set S)
3) 43 fruits altogether (set $\mathcal{E}$), 9 peaches (set P), 16 apples (set A)
4) 100 books altogether (set $\mathcal{E}$), 19 history books (set H), 28 science books (set S)
5) 22 people altogether (set $\mathcal{E}$), 12 boys (set B), 10 girls (set G)

---

c For each group of sets, draw a Venn diagram with the same pattern as the one on page 26 **C**. Place the correct NUMBER OF MEMBERS in each region.

1) 42 cars altogether (set $\mathcal{E}$), 11 blue cars (set B), 10 French cars (set F), 4 blue French cars (set $B \cap F$)
2) 18 girls altogether (set $\mathcal{E}$), 6 girls in the orchestra (set O), 5 girls in the netball team (set N), 3 girls in both the orchestra and the netball team (set $O \cap N$)
3) 21 cities altogether (set $\mathcal{E}$), 6 capital cities (set C), 7 German cities (set G), 2 German capital cities (set $G \cap C$)
4) 15 boys altogether (set $\mathcal{E}$), 4 boys play ONLY soccer (set $S \cap R'$), 3 boys play ONLY rugger (set $R \cap S'$), 2 boys play neither soccer nor rugger (set $(S \cup R)'$)
5) 17 castles altogether (set $\mathcal{E}$), 12 ruined castles (set R), 10 Scottish castles (set S), 8 ruined Scottish castles (set $R \cap S$).

A SETS (9)
Using a Venn Diagram (2)

e.g. This Venn diagram shows the NUMBER of members of each set.

$\mathcal{E}$ = {pupils}

F = {pupils who play football}

H = {pupils who play hockey}

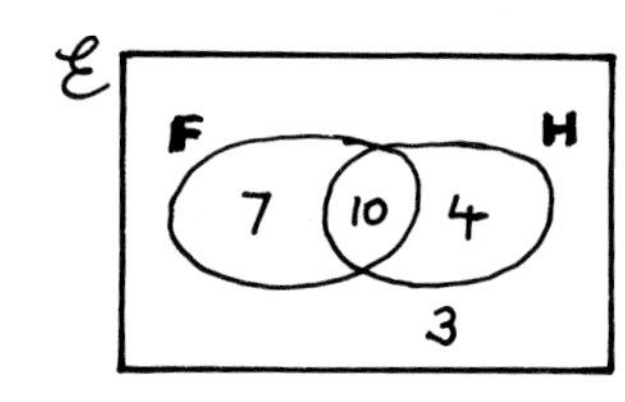

24 pupils altogether	n ($\mathcal{E}$) = 24
17 play football	n (F) = 17
14 play hockey	n (H) = 14
10 play both football and hockey	n (F $\cap$ H) = 10

*Fill in the INTERSECTION first. Then, if 10 pupils play both football and hockey, (17-10) = 7 play ONLY football, and (14-10) = 4 play ONLY hockey. This makes a total of (7+10+4) = 21 so (24-21) = 3 play NEITHER football nor hockey.

e.g. (2) $\mathcal{E}$ = {cows}, C = {contented cows}
F = {fat cows}, J = {Jersey cows}

55 cows altogether
36 contented cows
20 fat cows
27 Jersey cows

11 are fat contented Jersey cows
3 are not Jersey cows, but they are fat and contented
6 are contented Jersey cows which are not fat
2 are fat Jersey cows which are not contented

This leaves (36 - 11 - 3 - 6) = 16 contented cows which are not fat and are not Jerseys,
and (20 - 11 - 3 - 2) = 4 fat cows which are not contented and not Jerseys,
and (27 - 11 - 6 - 2) = 8 Jersey cows which are neither fat nor contented,
and (55 - 11 - 3 - 6 - 2 - 16 - 4 - 8) = 5 cows which are not contented, not fat and not Jerseys.

IN EACH OF THESE QUESTIONS, DRAW A VENN DIAGRAM AND PLACE THE NUMBERS IN THE CORRECT REGIONS. FOR QUESTIONS 1, 2, 3, 4 DRAW A DIAGRAM LIKE THE ONE ON PAGE 28 **A**; FOR QUESTION 5 DRAW ONE LIKE 28 **B**.

a

1) $\mathcal{E}$ = {people altogether}, I = {Indians}, W = {women}
9 people were Indian women
7 people were Indians but not women
14 people were women but not Indians
18 people were neither Indians nor women
(a) How many Indians were there altogether?
(b) How many people were there altogether?

---

2) $\mathcal{E}$ = {boys}, P = {boys who played the piano},
R = {boys who played the recorder},
30 boys altogether, 11 played only the piano, 8 played both piano and recorder, 7 played neither.
(a) How many played only the recorder?
(b) How many altogether played the piano?

---

3) $\mathcal{E}$ = {people}, H = {people wearing hats},
U = {people carrying umbrellas}
12 people wearing hats, 10 people carrying umbrellas, 7 people wearing hats and carrying umbrellas, 19 people neither wearing hats nor carrying umbrellas.
(a) How many people altogether?
(b) How many people wearing hats but not carrying umbrellas?

---

4) $\mathcal{E}$ = {cars}, G = {green cars}, R = {cars fitted with radios}
30 cars, 11 were green cars fitted with radios, altogether 19 cars were fitted with radios, 4 green cars were not fitted with radios
(a) How many cars were fitted with radios but were not green?
(b) How many cars without radios were not green?

---

5) $\mathcal{E}$ = {girls}, T = {tall girls}, E = {English girls},
I = {intelligent girls}
38 girls, 20 are English, 11 are tall, 27 are intelligent, 4 are tall intelligent English girls, 5 are tall and English but not intelligent, 10 are intelligent English girls who are not tall; 2 are tall but are not English and not intelligent.
(a) How many girls are neither English nor intelligent?
(b) How many girls are not tall, not English and not intelligent?
(c) How many tall, intelligent non-English girls are there?

HOURS, MINUTES, SECONDS

A Fractions of an hour

1 minute = $\frac{1}{60}$ hour
2 minutes = $\frac{\cancel{2}}{\cancel{60}}$ = $\frac{1}{30}$ hour, etc.

To convert minutes into fractions of an hour

e.g. Express 35 minutes as a fraction of 1 hour

*1) Divide by 60 $\frac{35}{60}$

*2) Cancel to lowest terms $\frac{\cancel{35}}{\cancel{60}}$ = $\frac{7}{12}$ hour

e.g. (2) Express 4 hours 40 minutes as a number of hours

$4\frac{40}{60} = 4\frac{\cancel{40}^2}{\cancel{60}_3} = 4\frac{2}{3}$ hours

---

B

To convert fractions of an hour into minutes

e.g. Convert $\frac{5}{6}$ hour into minutes

*1) Multiply by 60 $\frac{5}{6} \times \frac{60}{1}$

*2) Cancel as far as you can $\frac{5}{\cancel{6}_1} \times \frac{\cancel{60}^{10}}{1}$ = 50 minutes

e.g. (2) What is $2\frac{4}{5}$ hours in hours and minutes?

$2\frac{4}{5}$ hours = 2 hours $\frac{4}{\cancel{5}_1} \times \frac{\cancel{60}^{12}}{1}$ minutes

= 2 hours 48 minutes

60 minutes = 1 hour   60 min = 1 h
60 seconds = 1 minute   60 s = 1 min
3600 seconds = 1 hour   3600 s = 1 h

Conversion

hours to minutes	× 60
minutes to hours	÷ 60
minutes to seconds	× 60
seconds to minutes	÷ 60
hours to seconds	× 3600
seconds to hours	÷ 3600

e.g. Express 11 minutes in seconds   11 × 60 = 660 seconds

a

Express each of these as a fraction of 1 hour in its lowest terms

1) 12 minutes
2) 55 minutes
3) 30 minutes
4) 8 minutes
5) 20 minutes
6) 25 minutes
7) 3 minutes
8) 24 minutes
9) 45 minutes
10) 33 minutes
11) 13 minutes
12) 40 minutes
13) 15 minutes
14) 10 minutes
15) 54 minutes

b

Express each of these in **hours and fractions of an hour**

1) 3h 50min
2) 1h 16min
3) 5h 42 min
4) 6h 4 min
5) 2h 45 min
6) 10h 35min
7) 1h 20min
8) 7h 48min
9) 2h 5min
10) 3h 40min
11) 5h 30min
12) 8h 6min
13) 9h 44min
14) 12h 40 min
15) 4h 32 min

c

Express each of these in minutes

1) $\frac{1}{4}$ hour
2) $\frac{7}{12}$ hour
3) $\frac{4}{5}$ hour
4) $\frac{3}{10}$ hour
5) $\frac{1}{2}$ hour
6) $\frac{41}{60}$ hour
7) $\frac{2}{3}$ hour
8) $\frac{1}{6}$ hour
9) $\frac{11}{12}$ hour
10) $\frac{1}{3}$ hour
11) $\frac{9}{10}$ hour
12) $\frac{1}{12}$ hour
13) $\frac{17}{20}$ hour
14) $\frac{7}{60}$ hour
15) $\frac{13}{15}$ hour

d

Express each of these in **hours and minutes**
e.g. $5\frac{1}{4}$ hours = 5 hours 15 minutes

1) $3\frac{3}{4}$ hours
2) $2\frac{1}{3}$ hours
3) $6\frac{7}{12}$ hours
4) $4\frac{1}{4}$ hours
5) $1\frac{31}{60}$ hours
6) $5\frac{5}{6}$ hours
7) $2\frac{7}{10}$ hours
8) $7\frac{3}{5}$ hours
9) $4\frac{11}{20}$ hours
10) $1\frac{7}{15}$ hours
11) $10\frac{2}{3}$ hours
12) $8\frac{1}{2}$ hours
13) $3\frac{1}{6}$ hours
14) $5\frac{4}{15}$ hours
15) $1\frac{4}{5}$ hours

e

1) Express as a number of minutes
(a) 4 hours (b) 9 hours (c) $2\frac{1}{4}$ hours (d) $3\frac{3}{10}$ hours
(e) $1\frac{3}{5}$ hours

2) Express as a number of seconds
(a) 7 minutes (b) 3 minutes (c) $1\frac{1}{2}$ minutes
(d) $5\frac{1}{3}$ minutes (e) $\frac{3}{4}$ hour

3) Express as a number of minutes
(a) 120 seconds (b) 200 seconds (c) $4\frac{5}{6}$ hours
(d) 65 seconds (e) 395 seconds

4) Express as a number of hours
(a) 480 minutes (b) 210 minutes (c) 340 minutes
(d) 4200 seconds (e) 175 minutes

SPEED (1)

SPEED = DISTANCE ÷ TIME $S = \frac{D}{T}$

e.g. A ball, travelling at a steady speed, goes 100 metres in 5 seconds. What is its speed?

FIRST Write out values of DISTANCE and TIME $D = 100, T = 5$

THEN Work out speed $S = \frac{100}{5} = 20$

Ball travels at 20 m/s

Note Speeds are always written in **distance per time** units, e.g. m/s (metres per second), miles/h (miles per hour), etc.

Uniform speed and average speed

Things which travel at the same speed all the time have a UNIFORM SPEED (or STEADY SPEED).

Most things which move in the real world (trains, people, aeroplanes, tennis balls, spiders, etc.) do NOT travel at uniform speed, but you can still find their AVERAGE SPEED by the same formula.

$$S = \frac{D}{T}$$

e.g. A train went 380 miles in 5 hours. What was its average speed?

$$D = 380 \quad , \quad T = 5$$

$$S = \frac{380}{5} = 76$$

Average speed of the train was 76 miles/h

Hours and minutes

Always express hours and minutes in HOURS AND FRACTIONS OF AN HOUR (unless the question asks you to work in minutes). Look at page 30A if you are not sure.

e.g. What is the average speed of a car which travels 132 miles in 2h 45min?

$$D = 132 , \quad T = 2\tfrac{3}{4}$$

$$S = 132 \div 2\tfrac{3}{4} = \frac{132}{1} \div \frac{11}{4} = 48 \text{ miles/h}$$

a Find the speed (S) from each distance (D) and time (T)

1) D = 35 m, T = 5 s
2) D = 630 miles, T = 7 h
3) D = 48 km, T = 3 h
4) D = 8 m, T = 0.2 s
5) D = 64.5 m, T = 5 min
6) D = 506 miles, T = 22 h
7) D = 65 km, T = 2½ h
8) D = 49 m, T = 3½ s
9) D = 405 miles, T = 13½ h
10) D = 5340 km, T = 12 h

---

b Find the average speed of

1) a boy who walks 27 miles in 9 hours
2) a boat which travels 84 km in 6 hours
3) a cricket ball which travels 138 metres in 6 seconds
4) a girl who cycles 72 miles in 4½ hours
5) an aeroplane which flies 1008 miles in 5¼ hours
6) a snail which goes 4 metres in 8 minutes
7) a yacht which sails 12 miles in 1⅓ hours
8) a bee which flies 44 metres in 8 seconds
9) a locomotive which travels 208 miles in 2⅔ hours
10) an athlete who runs 400 metres in 64 seconds

---

c Find the average speed of

1) an airliner which travels 910 miles in 2 hours 30 minutes
2) a car which travels 105 miles in 2 hours 20 minutes
3) a boy who walks 13½ miles in 3 h 45 min
4) a train which travels 490 miles in 5 h 50 min
5) a ship which goes 88 km in 3 h 40 min
6) a man who cycles 31½ miles in 2 h 15 min
7) a train which goes 400 miles in 4 h 10 min
8) a pigeon which flies 137½ km in 2 h 5 min
9) a helicopter which sets off at 13 15 and travels 120 miles, ending its journey at 14 55
10) a bus which departs from Spalding at 18 45 and arrives at Melton Mowbray, 36 miles away, at 20 21

A

SPEED (2)

Finding DISTANCE

DISTANCE = SPEED × TIME $\qquad$ D = ST

e.g. A car travels for 5 hours at a speed of 38 miles/hour. How far does it travel ?

S = 38

T = 5 $\qquad$ D = 38 × 5 = 190 miles

e.g. (2) An aeroplane flies at a speed of 474 km/h for 3 hours 10 minutes. How far does it fly?

S = 474

$T = 3\frac{1}{6}$ $\qquad$ $D = 474 \times 3\frac{1}{6} = \frac{474}{1} \times \frac{19}{6} = 1501$ km

---

B

Finding TIME

TIME = DISTANCE ÷ SPEED $\qquad$ $T = \frac{D}{S}$

e.g. A bird flew a distance of 105 miles at an average speed of 15 miles/h. How long did its journey take?

D = 105

S = 15 $\qquad$ $T = \frac{105}{15} = 7$ hours

e.g. (2) A train travelled from Darlington to London, a distance of 232 miles, at an average speed of 80 miles/h. How long, in hours and minutes, did it take?

D = 232

S = 80

$T = \frac{232}{80} = \frac{29}{10} = 2\frac{9}{10}$ hours

$= 2$ hours $(\frac{9}{10} \times \frac{60}{1})$ minutes

$= 2$ hours 54 minutes

REMEMBER To change a fraction of an hour into minutes, multiply by 60 (see page 30B).

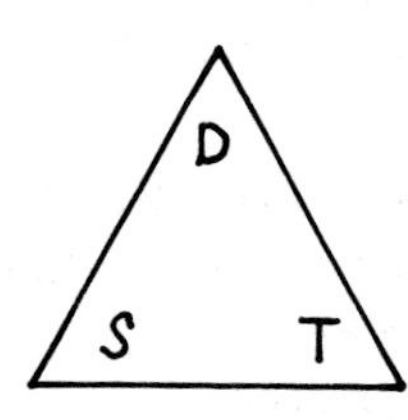

D = ST $\qquad$ (speed × time)

$S = \frac{D}{T}$ $\qquad$ (distance ÷ time)

$T = \frac{D}{S}$ $\qquad$ (distance ÷ speed)

a ALWAYS READ THE QUESTION CAREFULLY AND MAKE SURE WHAT YOU HAVE BEEN ASKED TO FIND. Is it SPEED, or DISTANCE, or TIME?

1) Steven walked for 3 hours at an average speed of 5 km/h. What distance did he walk?

2) A boy ran 200 metres at a speed of 5 m/s. How long did it take him?

3) Barbara cycled at an average speed of 13 miles/h. If her journey took $2\frac{1}{2}$ hours, how far did she go?

4) A golf ball travelled a distance of 27 m at a speed of 36 m/s. How long did it take?

5) An aircraft flew 880 miles at a speed of 330 miles/h. How long, in hours and minutes, did its journey take?

6) A train travels for 4 h 45 min at an average speed of 84 miles/h. Calculate the distance it travels.

7) Bert drove his truck from Exeter to Manchester a distance of 240 miles, in 5 hours 20 minutes. What was his average speed?

8) Kathy and Sara went on a $16\frac{1}{2}$ mile hike. Their average walking speed was $2\frac{3}{4}$ miles/h. How long did it take them?

9) Light travels at about 186000 mile/s. The sun is about 93 000 000 miles from Earth. About how many seconds does it take sunlight to reach the Earth?

10) A motorist drove from Girvan to Edinburgh in 2 hours 40 minutes at an average speed of $34\frac{1}{2}$ miles/h. Find the distance from Girvan to Edinburgh.

11) Mohammed and his uncle travelled from Liverpool to Nottingham, a distance of 99 miles, in 2 hours 45 minutes. What was their average speed?

12) A snail, travelling at $13\frac{1}{2}$ m/hour, went from the wheelbarrow to the plastic gnome $5\frac{2}{5}$ m away. How long, in minutes, did its journey take?

13) A bottle containing a message was launched from St. Kilda island on March 23 and reached Stromness, after floating 242 miles, on May 6. What was the average speed of the bottle in miles/day?

14) Angela set off on her motorbike at 3.46 p.m. and rode at an average speed of 48 miles/h until 4.21 p.m. By first finding how long, in hours, she took, calculate how far she went.

15) A train leaves Glasgow at 08 20 and travels 88 miles to Taynuilt at an average speed of $31\frac{3}{7}$ miles/h. At what time does it reach Taynuilt?

A SPEED (3)
Average speed

$$\text{AVERAGE SPEED} = \frac{\text{Total distance}}{\text{Total time}}$$

e.g. (1) A man cycled a distance of 30 miles in 2½ hours, then walked 6 miles in 1½ hours. What was his average speed for the whole journey?

Total distance = 30 + 6 = 36 miles
Total time = 2½ + 1½ = 4 hours

Average speed = $\frac{36}{4}$ = 9 miles/hour

---

e.g. (2) Karen walked 7½ miles in 2 hours 10 minutes. Then she travelled a further 6¼ miles by bus. The bus took 20 minutes. Find her average speed for the whole journey.

Total distance = 7½ + 6¼ = 13¾ miles
Total time = 2 h 10 min + 20 min = 2 h 30 min = 2½ hours

Average speed = $\frac{13\frac{3}{4}}{2\frac{1}{2}}$ = 13¾ ÷ 2½ = $\frac{55}{4} \div \frac{5}{2}$

= $\frac{\overset{11}{\cancel{55}}}{\underset{2}{\cancel{4}}} \times \frac{\overset{1}{\cancel{2}}}{\underset{1}{\cancel{5}}}$ = 5½ miles/hour

---

e.g. (3) James travelled on a train for 2 hours 10 minutes at an average speed of 66 miles/hour. Then he went by taxi for 30 minutes at an average speed of 34 miles/hour. By finding the total distance he travelled, calculate his average speed for the whole journey.

Train Distance = Speed × Time 66 × 2⅙ = 143 miles

Taxi Distance = Speed × Time 34 × ½ = 17 miles

Total distance = 143 + 17 = 160 miles
Total time = 2⅙ + ½ = 2⅔ miles

Average speed = 160 ÷ 2⅔ = 60 miles/hour

a

1) Paul ran 420m in 119 seconds and then walked 160m in 171 seconds. What was his average speed?

2) A car travelled 145 miles in 4 hours, then 83 miles in 2 hours. Find its average speed for the whole journey.

3) Naomi and Rachel left school at 1603 and walked to the bus stop, arriving there at 1619, just in time to catch the bus which took 32 minutes to reach their house. The distance from the school to their house was 12 miles. Find their average speed in miles/hour for the whole journey.

4) Edward cycled 31km in 1 hour 10 minutes. Then he walked 11km in 2 hours 20 minutes. Find his average speed for the whole journey.

5) A tennis ball travelled a distance of 61 metres through the air for $2\frac{1}{2}$ seconds. Then it rolled 44m along the ground for 5 seconds. Calculate its average speed.

6) Christine travelled 39 miles by train. The journey took 55 minutes. She then went by car for another 9 miles, taking a further 17 minutes. What was her average speed, in miles/hour, for the complete journey?

7) An aeroplane made a journey in two stages. The first stage, at an average speed of 324km/h, was completed in 40 minutes. The second stage, at an average speed of 296km/h, was completed in 30 minutes. What was its average speed for the whole journey?

8) A bus went from Salisbury to Exeter. It travelled for 1h 10min at an average speed of 27 miles/h. Then it travelled for 25min at an average speed of 42 miles/h. By finding both distances, calculate the total distance from Salisbury to Exeter.

9) A train travelled for 1h 15min at 76 miles/h, and then for 45min at 84 miles/h. Find the two distances the train travelled and from your answers calculate the average speed of the train for the complete journey.

10) Adrian travelled from Cambridge to London,a distance of 55 miles, at an average speed of 60 miles/hour. He returned to Cambridge at an average speed of 30 miles/hour. What was his average speed from Cambridge to London and back?

SPEED (4)
A Conversions

e.g. Express a speed of 20m/s in km/h

3600 seconds = 1 hour 1000 metres = 1 kilometre

In 1 second the distance covered is 20 metres, so in 1 hour the distance covered is $20 \times 3600 = 72000$ metres

$$72000 \text{ metres} = \frac{72\,000}{1000} = 72 \text{ kilometres}$$

so a speed of 20 m/s = <u>72 km/h</u>

---

e.g. (2) An airliner travels at a speed of 576 km/h. What is its speed in metres/second?

1000 metres = 1 kilometre 3600 seconds = 1 hour

In 1 hour it travels $576 \times 1000 = 576\,000$ m

so in 1 second it travels $\frac{576\,000}{3600} = 160$ m

Airliner's speed is <u>160 metres/second</u>

---

e.g. (3) Express 4.2 m/min in cm/sec

100 centimetres = 1 metre 60 seconds = 1 minute

4.2 m/min

$= 4.2 \times 100 = 420 \text{ cm/min} = \frac{420}{60}$

= <u>7 cm/sec</u>

---

e.g. (4) Express 2.25 cm/s in km/h

3600 seconds = 1 hour 100 000 centimetres = 1 kilometre

$2.25 \text{ cm/s} = 2.25 \times 3600 = 8100 \text{ cm/h}$

$= \frac{8100}{100\,000}$

= <u>0.081 km/h</u>

a

A man walked at 2 metres/second.

1) How many metres did he walk in an hour?
2) How many kilometres did he walk in an hour?
3) What was his speed in kilometres/hour?

A train travelled at 108 kilometres/hour.

4) How many metres did it travel in an hour?
5) What was its speed in metres/second?

---

b

Express in km/h

1) 5 m/s
2) 12 m/s
3) 40 m/s
4) 0.25 m/s
5) 100 m/s
6) 45 m/s
7) $1\frac{2}{3}$ m/s
8) $9\frac{1}{6}$ m/s
9) 18.5 m/s
10) N m/s

---

c

Express in m/s

1) 36 km/h
2) $4\frac{1}{2}$ km/h
3) 126 km/h
4) 1080 km/h
5) 2.7 km/h
6) 63 km/h
7) 66600 km/h
8) $\frac{4}{5}$ km/h
9) 414 km/h
10) Y km/h

---

d

By multiplying and/or dividing by the correct amounts, do these conversions.

1) Express 27 m/min in cm/s
2) Express 9 km/h in m/min
3) Write 219 m/min in cm/s
4) Express 55 m/s in km/hour
5) Write 70 cm/s in m/min
6) An aeroplane travelled at 486 km/h. What was its speed in m/s?
7) A boy walked at 5.4 km/h. Express his speed in cm/s
8) Sound travels through air at about 330 m/s. Express this speed in km/h
9) A sailing ship travelled at 450 metres/minute. What was its speed in km/h?
10) What is the speed in m/min of a giraffe which runs at 39 km/h?

---

cm = centimetres
h = hours
km = kilometres
m = metres
min = minutes
s = seconds

OTHER BASES (1)

Normal counting is done in **BASE 10** (also called DENARY or DECIMAL), i.e.

1, 2, 3, 4, 5, 6, 7, 8, 9, 10, 11, 12, 13, etc.

In BASE 10, TEN different figures (or digits) are used, i.e. 0,1,2,3,4,5,6,7,8 and 9

Counting in other bases can be just as easy
e.g. In **BASE 6**, six different figures are used
0, 1, 2, 3, 4 and 5

In BASE 6, no figure larger than 5 may be used, so counting in base 6 goes

1, 2, 3, 4, 5, 10, 11, 12, 13, 14, 15, 20, etc

e.g. In **BASE 2** (binary), two different figures are used
0, 1

In base 2 (binary) no figure larger than 1 may be used, so counting in base 2 goes

1, 10, 11, 100, 101, 110, 111, 1000, 1001, 1010, 1011, etc.

Base 2 is usually called BINARY
Base 3 is sometimes called TERNARY
Base 8 is sometimes called OCTAL

NOTE Bases can be larger than 10, e.g. base 16 (hexadecimal, but usually called just HEX), which is used in computing.
For bases larger than 10, new 'figures' must be invented, e.g. counting in base 16 goes 1, 2, 3, 4, 5, 6, 7, 8, 9, A, B, C, D, E, F, 10, 11, etc.

Columns in other bases

The columns in ordinary counting (base 10) are

$\underline{10000}$ $\underline{1000}$ $\underline{100}$ $\underline{10}$ $\underline{1}$

Each column is multiplied by $\underline{10}$ to get the next bigger column.
In other bases each column is multiplied BY THE BASE to get the next column, e.g. in base 4

4^4	4^3	4^2	4^1	4^0	
(64×4)	(16×4)	(4×4)	(1×4)		
$\underline{256}$	$\underline{64}$	$\underline{16}$	$\underline{4}$	$\underline{1}$	etc.

IMPORTANT. The right-hand column is always the UNITS COLUMN (the ONES column) in any base.

a e.g. Write down the first fifteen numbers in base 5, starting with 1

Answer 1,2,3,4,10,11,12,13,14,20,21,22,23,24,30

Write down, starting with 1,

1) the first ten numbers in base 3

2) the first twenty numbers in base 8

3) the first ten numbers in base 4

4) the first fifteen numbers in base 7

5) the first twenty numbers in base 9

---

b e.g. Find the next five consecutive numbers above 14 in base 7

Answer 15, 16, 20, 21, 22

1) Find the next four consecutive numbers above 26 in base 8

2) Find the next five consecutive numbers above 1212 in base 3

3) Find the next three consecutive numbers below 61 in base 7

4) Find the next four consecutive numbers above 42 in base 5

5) Find the next four consecutive numbers below 122 in base 6

---

c e.g. Find the values of $7^3, 7^2, 7^1, 7^0$, and set them out as columns in base 7

$7^3 = 7 \times 7 \times 7 = 343$; $7^2 = 7 \times 7 = 49$; $7^1 = 7$; $7^0 = 1$

so answer is $\underline{343}$ $\underline{49}$ $\underline{7}$ $\underline{1}$

REMEMBER. Anything to the power 0 = 1

e.g. $4^0 = 1$, $8^0 = 1$, etc.

In each of these, find the values of the numbers and set out the answers in columns

1) $8^3, 8^2, 8^1, 8^0$

2) $3^6, 3^5, 3^4, 3^3, 3^2, 3^1, 3^0$

3) $2^7, 2^6, 2^5, 2^4, 2^3, 2^2, 2^1, 2^0$

4) $10^5, 10^4, 10^3, 10^2, 10^1, 10^0$

5) $12^2, 12^1, 12^0$

---

d e.g. Work out the first five columns in base 3

Answer $\underline{81}$ $\underline{27}$ $\underline{9}$ $\underline{3}$ $\underline{1}$

Work out the first five columns in

1) base 6

2) base 4

3) base 9

4) base 7

5) base 5

OTHER BASES (2)

The base of a number is written at the bottom after the number

e.g. 213 in base 5 is written 213_5

1011001 in binary is written 1011001_2

48 in base 10 (ordinary counting) is written 48_{10}

Converting TO denary

To convert an 'other base' number into a denary (ordinary) number, e.g. Convert 1232_4 into denary

*1) Write the columns of the other base **64 16 4 1**

*2) Place numbers in correct columns 1 2 3 2

(Remember. The right hand figure is always the UNITS)

*3) Work out each column

$1 \times 64 = 64$
$2 \times 16 = 32$
$3 \times 4 = 12$
$2 \times 1 = 2$

*4) Add all the answers $64 + 32 + 12 + 2 = 110$

so $1232_4 = 110_{10}$

Other examples

1) Convert 76_8 into denary

8	1
7	6

$7 \times 8 = 56$
$6 \times 1 = 6+$
62_{10}

2) Convert 1243_5 to base 10

125	25	5	1
1	2	4	3

$1 \times 125 = 125$
$2 \times 25 = 50$
$4 \times 5 = 20$
$3 \times 1 = 3+$
198_{10}

3) Convert 101101_2 to denary

32	16	8	4	2	1
1	0	1	1	0	1

$1 \times 32 = 32$
$0 \times 16 = 0$
$1 \times 8 = 8$
$1 \times 4 = 4$
$0 \times 2 = 0$
$1 \times 1 = 1+$
45_{10}

a

Write in short

e.g. 517 in base 9 = 517_9

1) 1010 in base 3
2) 62 in base 8
3) 345 in base 10
4) 1232 in base 5
5) 523 in base 7
6) 41 in base 9
7) 987 in base 11
8) 110111 in binary
9) 223 in base 4
10) 722 in octal

---

b

Convert each of these base 8 numbers to denary (base 10)

1) 31_8
2) 54_8
3) 65_8
4) 143_8
5) 77_8
6) 306_8
7) 222_8
8) 460_8
9) 1115_8
10) 544_8

---

c

Express these binary (base 2) numbers in denary (base 10)

1) 101_2
2) 1110_2
3) 1001_2
4) 11011_2
5) 10010_2
6) 111001_2
7) 11111_2
8) 101010_2
9) 11100_2
10) 1000000_2

---

d

Convert these numbers into denary

1) 13_6
2) 42_8
3) 24_5
4) 57_9
5) 1230_4
6) 121_3
7) 56_7
8) 102_5
9) 223_6
10) 212_4
11) 163_7
12) 1202_3
13) 142_9
14) 11101_2
15) 255_6
16) 86_9
17) 131_4
18) 267_8
19) 2211_3
20) 324_6

---

e

Express in denary

1) 111_7
2) 484_9
3) 1230_5
4) 20221_3
5) 2123_4
6) 523_8
7) 68_{11}
8) 1101100_2
9) 1433_6
10) 2411_5
11) 1432_8
12) 12121_3
13) 94_{13}
14) 246_9
15) 1000_6
16) 3032_4
17) 514_7
18) 100111_2
19) 636_8
20) 22020_3

OTHER BASES (3)

A Converting FROM denary

To convert an ordinary (denary, or base 10) number into an 'other base' number

e.g. Convert 73_{10} into base 6

*1) Divide the number by the base and write the remainder after the answer. Make sure there is a good gap between the answer and the remainder

6	73	
	12	r.1

*2) Repeat until the answer is 0

6	73	
6	12	r.1 ↑
6	2	r.0
	0	r.2

*3) Read the remainders from the bottom upwards $= \underline{201_6}$

REMEMBER

1) There cannot be a remainder on the top line.

2) If there is no remainder, write 0

3) The **bottom remainder** is always the same figure as the **next-to-bottom answer**

e.g. Write 345_{10} as a number in base 5

5	345	
5	69	0 ↑
5	13	4
5	**2**	3
	0	**2**

$= \underline{2340_5}$

Other examples

1) Convert 77_{10} to binary

2	77	
2	38	1 ↑
2	19	0
2	9	1
2	4	1
2	2	0
2	1	0
	0	1

$77_{10} = \underline{1001101_2}$

2) Express 171_{10} in base 8

8	171	
8	21	3 ↑
8	2	5
	0	2

$171_{10} = \underline{253_8}$

3) Write the denary number 86 as a number in base 3

3	86	
3	28	2 ↑
3	9	1
3	3	0
3	1	0
	0	1

$86_{10} = \underline{10012_3}$

a

Write these denary numbers in base 5

1) 23_{10} *3)* 49_{10} *5)* 57_{10} *7)* 78_{10} *9)* 115_{10}
2) 66_{10} *4)* 125_{10} *6)* 6_{10} *8)* 196_{10} *10)* 1276_{10}

b

Write these denary numbers in base 8

1) 38_{10} *3)* 58_{10} *5)* 95_{10} *7)* 973_{10} *9)* 155_{10}
2) 107_{10} *4)* 136_{10} *6)* 338_{10} *8)* 52_{10} *10)* 513_{10}

c

Express these denary numbers in binary (base 2)

1) 7_{10} *6)* 44_{10} *11)* 21_{10} *16)* 72_{10}
2) 36_{10} *7)* 80_{10} *12)* 100_{10} *17)* 29_{10}
3) 24_{10} *8)* 63_{10} *13)* 55_{10} *18)* 49_{10}
4) 11_{10} *9)* 9_{10} *14)* 16_{10} *19)* 18_{10}
5) 39_{10} *10)* 128_{10} *15)* 5_{10} *20)* 31_{10}

d

Write

1) 28_{10} in base 6
2) 141_{10} in base 9
3) 55_{10} in base 3
4) 99_{10} in base 7
5) 47_{10} in base 2
6) 321_{10} in base 9
7) 73_{10} in base 4
8) 118_{10} in base 6
9) 277_{10} in base 5
10) 115_{10} in base 8
11) 89_{10} in base 3
12) 233_{10} in base 8
13) 44_{10} in base 5
14) 285_{10} in base 7
15) 39_{10} in base 4

e

For converting **other bases into denary (base 10)**, see page 42 B
For converting **denary (base 10) into other bases**, see page 44 A

1) 212_{10} to base 5
2) 191_{10} to base 7
3) 2100_3 to denary
4) 62_{10} to base 4
5) 3313_4 to base 10
6) 402_6 to denary
7) 91_{10} to base 2
8) 432_5 to denary
9) 606_{10} to base 9
10) 101110_2 to base 10
11) 350_9 to denary
12) 479_{10} to base 6
13) 111_{10} to base 3
14) 623_7 to base 10
15) 340_{10} to base 8

A OTHER BASES (4) +ADDITION

If no 'carrying' is needed, do just like a normal (base 10) addition e.g.

$$\begin{array}{r} 124_6 \\ +230_6 \\ \hline 354_6 \end{array}$$

B 'Carrying'

HOW MANY GROUPS AND HOW MANY LEFT OVER?

e.g. Add in BASE 7 : $236_7 + 154_7$

*How many groups of 7 and how many left over? $6 + 4 =$ **10** which is 1 group of 7 with 3 left over.

Write down 3 and 'carry' 1

$$\begin{array}{rrr} 2 & 3 & 6 \\ +1 & 5 & 4 \\ \hline & {}^{1} & 3 \end{array}$$

*How many groups of 7 and how many left over? $3 + 5 + 1 =$ **9** which is 1 group of 7 with 2 left over.

Write down 2 and 'carry' 1

$$\begin{array}{rrr} 2 & 3 & 6 \\ +1 & 5 & 4 \\ \hline {}^{1} & 2 & 3 \end{array}$$

$$\begin{array}{rrr} 2 & 3 & 6 \\ +1 & 5 & 4 \\ \hline 4 & 2 & 3_7 \end{array}$$

Answer 423_7

e.g. Add in BASE 8

$$\begin{array}{rrrr} & 7 & 6 & 5 \\ & 2 & 4 & 7 \\ + & & 6 & 2 \\ \hline & & {}^{1} & 6 \end{array}$$

1 group of 8 with 6 left over

$$\begin{array}{rrrr} & 7 & 6 & 5 \\ & 2 & 4 & 7 \\ + & & 6 & 2 \\ \hline & {}^{2} & 1 & 6 \end{array}$$

2 groups of 8 with 1 left over

$$\begin{array}{rrrr} & 7 & 6 & 5 \\ & 2 & 4 & 7 \\ + & & 6 & 2 \\ \hline 1 & 3 & 1 & 6 \end{array}$$

1 group of 8 with 3 left over

Answer 1316_8

e.g. $2124_5 + 1243_5 + 104_5$

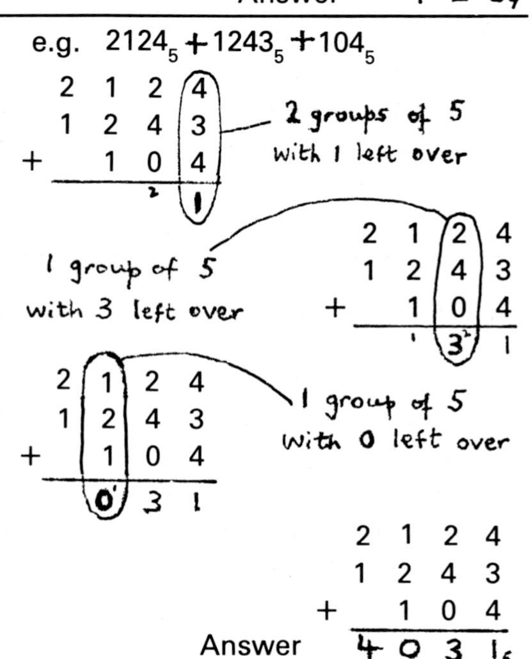

a Try these additions in base 8

1) $532_8 + 213_8$
2) $634_8 + 53_8$
3) $25_8 + 364_8$
4) $743_8 + 61_8$
5) $626_8 + 503_8$
6) $35_8 + 24_8 + 23_8$
7) $135_8 + 542_8$
8) $5326_8 + 737_8$
9) $540_8 + 456_8$
10) $446_8 + 545_8 + 612_8$

---

b

1) Add in base 7 : $514_7 + 634_7$
2) Add in base 3 : $1201_3 + 2102_3 + 221_3$
3) Add in base 5 : $314_5 + 240_5$
4) Add in base 9 : $13_9 + 562_9 + 438_9$
5) Add in base 4 : $123_4 + 201_4 + 22_4$

---

c

1) Add 713_8, 56_8, 101_8
2) Add 5232_6, 504_6
3) Add 1676_{10}, 835_{10}, 2131_{10}
4) Add 22_7, 1520_7, 413_7
5) Find the sum of 10101_3, 2012_3, 11212_3

---

d Try these additions

1) $242_5 + 134_5$
2) $1123_4 + 332_4$
3) $462_9 + 813_9 + 76_9$
4) $1452_6 + 3134_6$
5) $10011_2 + 110_2 + 1011_2$
6) $63_8 + 1620_8 + 377_8$
7) $53_6 + 44_6 + 25_6 + 32_6$
8) $501_7 + 342_7 + 64_7$
9) $975_{11} + 287_{11}$
10) $20_3 + 1120_3 + 212_3$

---

e

1) $663_7 + 4425_7$
2) $516_8 + 2032_8 + 621_8$
3) $210_3 + 112_3 + 212_3$
4) $330_6 + 52_6 + 1413_6$
5) $16_9 + 53_9 + 7_9 + 72_9$
6) $3402_5 + 2131_5 + 1234_5$
7) $853_{12} + 74_{12} + 708_{12}$
8) $1002_4 + 1133_4 + 321_4$
9) $64_8 + 26_8 + 35_8$
10) $302_5 + 130_5 + 3213_5$
11) $67_9 + 75_9 + 82_9$
12) $1101_2 + 111_2 + 10111_2$
13) $703_{10} + 48_{10} + 189_{10}$
14) $202_4 + 33_4 + 21_4$
15) $425_6 + 433_6$

A OTHER BASES (5) —SUBTRACTION

If no 'borrowing' is needed, do just like a normal (base 10) subtraction, e.g.

$$\begin{array}{r} 546_8 \\ -204_8 \\ \hline 342_8 \end{array}$$

'Borrowing'

Borrow ONE GROUP from the next column

e.g. Subtract in BASE 6 : $42_6 - 15_6$

*2 subtract 5 is not possible, so 'borrow' a group of 6 from the next column. Now instead of '2 subtract 5' you have '8 subtract 5'

$$\begin{array}{rr} \overset{3}{\not 4} & \overset{8}{\not 2} \\ -1 & 5 \\ \hline & 3 \end{array} \qquad \begin{array}{rr} \overset{3}{\not 4} & \not 2^{8} \\ -1 & 5 \\ \hline 2 & 3_6 \end{array}$$

---

e.g. Subtract 156_7 from 324_7

*4 subtract 6 is not possible, so 'borrow' a group of 7 from the next column. Now you have '11 subtract 6'

*1 subtract 5 is not possible, so 'borrow' a group of 7 from the next column. Now you have '8 subtract 5'

$$\begin{array}{rrr} 3 & \overset{1}{\not 2} & \overset{11}{\not 4} \\ -1 & 5 & 6 \\ \hline & & 5 \end{array} \qquad \begin{array}{rrr} \overset{2}{\not 3} & \overset{8}{\not 1} & \not 4^{11} \\ -1 & 5 & 6 \\ \hline & 3 & 5 \end{array} \qquad \begin{array}{rrr} {}^{2}\not 3 & \overset{8}{\not 1} & \not 4^{11} \\ -1 & 5 & 6 \\ \hline 1 & 3 & 5_7 \end{array}$$

MIXED ADDITION AND SUBTRACTION

*Do each stage separately

e.g. $1212_3 + 221_3 - 2101_3$

$$\text{(a)} \quad \begin{array}{rrrr} 1' & 2' & 1' & 2 \\ + & 2 & 2 & 1 \\ \hline 2 & 2 & 1 & 0 \end{array} \qquad \text{(b)} \quad \begin{array}{rrrr} 2 & 2 & \not 1^{0} & \not 0^{3} \\ -2 & 1 & 0 & 1 \\ \hline & 1 & 0 & 2_3 \end{array}$$

a

Try these subtractions in base 5

1) $432_5 - 212_5$

2) $313_5 - 122_5$

3) $421_5 - 33_5$

4) $42_5 - 23_5$

5) $240_5 - 12_5$

6) $331_5 - 143_5$

7) $1242_5 - 423_5$

8) $303_5 - 34_5$

9) $30_5 - 12_5$

10) $1101_5 - 324_5$

---

b

Subtract in base 7

1) $625_7 - 113_7$
2) $434_7 - 216_7$
3) $305_7 - 252_7$
4) $542_7 - 66_7$
5) $24_7 - 5_7$
6) $1305_7 - 561_7$
7) $614_7 - 132_7$
8) $1160_7 - 524_7$
9) $512_7 - 443_7$
10) $1502_7 - 415_7$

---

c

1) $313_4 - 120_4$
2) $741_9 - 274_9$
3) $1321_5 - 341_5$
4) $5216_8 - 2142_8$
5) $2021_3 - 212_3$
6) $420_6 - 53_6$
7) $11101_2 - 1010_2$
8) $40_5 - 12_5$
9) $4110_8 - 1372_8$
10) $82_9 - 7_9$

---

d

1) Find the difference between 2623_8 and 747_8
2) Subtract 4432_7 from 5000_7
3) Find the difference between 6004_9 and 235_9
4) Subtract 1310_6 from 5425_6
5) Find the difference between 12021_3 and 1202_3

---

e

1) $132_4 + 1222_4$
2) $7101_8 - 465_8$
3) $2433_5 - 1144_5$
4) $1111_2 + 111_2 + 11_2$
5) $551_6 - 45_6$
6) $524_8 + 655_8 - 730_8$
7) $2211_3 - 1012_3 - 222_3$
8) $122_4 + 123_4 - 230_4$
9) $31_9 + 585_9 + 156_9$
10) $4131_5 - 1332_5 + 2201_5$

A OTHER BASES (6) ×MULTIPLICATION

This is like addition (see page 46)

'Carrying' HOW MANY GROUPS AND HOW MANY LEFT OVER?

e.g. Multiply in BASE 4 : $1321_4 \times 3$

```
    1 3 2 1
×         3
        2 3
```

6 (1 group of 4 with 2 left over)

```
    1 3 2 1
×         3
      2 2 3
```

9 + 1 to carry = 10 (2 groups of 4 with 2 left over)

```
    1 3 2 1
×         3
  1 1 2 2 3₄
```

3 + 2 to carry = 5 (1 group of 4 with 1 left over)

B LONG MULTIPLICATION

e.g. Multiply $87_9 \times 62_9$

```
    8 7
×   6 2
      5
```

14 (1 group of 9 with 5 left over)

```
    8 7
×   6 2
  1 8 5
```

16 + 1 to carry = 17 (1 group of 9 with 8 left over)

```
    8 7
×   6 2
  1 8 5
    6 0
```

42 (4 groups of 9 with 6 left over)

```
    8 7
×   6 2
  1 8 5
5 7 6 0
```

48 + 4 to carry = 52 (5 groups of 9 with 7 left over)

```
      8 7
×     6 2
    1 8 5
  5 7 6 0
  6 0 5 5₉
```

Then add answers **IN BASE 9**

$87_9 \times 62_9 = 6055_9$

a Multiply in base 7

1) $251_7 \times 5$
2) $46_7 \times 3$
3) $1043_7 \times 6$
4) $622_7 \times 4$
5) $361_7 \times 2$
6) $2342_7 \times 4$
7) $1241_7 \times 3$
8) $605_7 \times 6$
9) $2012_7 \times 3$
10) $513_7 \times 5$

---

b

1) $423_6 \times 3$
2) $2012_3 \times 2$
3) $576_8 \times 6$
4) $322_4 \times 3$
5) $1125_6 \times 4$
6) $572_9 \times 3$
7) $1323_5 \times 2$
8) $235_8 \times 4$
9) $221_3 \times 2$
10) $431_5 \times 4$
11) $304_6 \times 5$
12) $27_8 \times 7$
13) $1310_4 \times 3$
14) $268_{11} \times 9$
15) $64_9 \times 8$
16) $223_4 \times 2$
17) $1201_3 \times 2$
18) $1450_8 \times 5$
19) $2317_9 \times 5$
20) $142_5 \times 3$

---

c Do these by long multiplication

1) $34_5 \times 23_5$
2) $37_8 \times 43_8$
3) $120_3 \times 11_3$
4) $251_6 \times 14_6$
5) $72_9 \times 36_9$
6) $312_4 \times 12_4$
7) $36_7 \times 34_7$
8) $63_8 \times 26_8$
9) $11010_2 \times 11_2$
10) $42_6 \times 52_6$

---

d

1) $354_6 \times 44_6$
2) $211_3 \times 12_3$
3) $28_9 \times 14_9$
4) $1010_2 \times 101_2$
5) $64_7 \times 24_7$
6) $430_5 \times 41_5$
7) $115_8 \times 36_8$
8) $32_4 \times 31_4$
9) $534_7 \times 52_7$
10) $22_3 \times 21_3$

---

e

1) $123_4 \times 3$
2) $5465_8 + 764_8$
3) $2121_3 \times 22_3$
4) $503_7 - 346_7$
5) $35_6 + 454_6 + 125_6$
6) $136_8 \times 47_8$
7) $2221_3 + 1202_3$
8) $10110_2 - 1101_2$
9) $321_5 \times 34_5$
10) $520_9 - 173_9$

A OTHER BASES (7) ÷ DIVISION

Remainders are **GROUPS OF THE BASE** you are working in.

e.g. Divide 424_5 by 3

$3 \overline{)4\ 2^7\ 4}$ with quotient digit 1

$4 \div 3 = 1$, remainder 1 group of 5

This makes the next figure 2 + 5 = **7**

$3 \overline{)4\ 2^7\ 4^9}$ with quotient digits 1 2

$7 \div 3 = 2$, remainder 1 group of 5

This makes the next figure 4 + 5 = **9**

$3 \overline{)4\ 2^7\ 4^9}$ with quotient digits 1 2 3

$9 \div 3 = 3$

$= \underline{123_5}$

---

e.g. (2) $1426_8 \div 5$

$5 \overline{)1\ 4^{12}\ 2\ 6}$ with quotient digit 0

$1 \div 5 = 0$, remainder 1 group of 8
making next figure $4 + 8 = 12$

$5 \overline{)1\ 4^{12}\ 2^{18}\ 6}$ with quotient digits 0 2

$12 \div 5 = 2$, remainder 2 groups of 8
making next figure $2+8+8 = 18$

$5 \overline{)1\ 4^{12}\ 2^{18}\ 6}$ with quotient digits 0 2 3

$18 \div 5 = 3$, remainder 3 groups of 8
making next figure $6+8+8+8 = 30$

$5 \overline{)1\ 4^{12}\ 2^{18}\ 6^{30}}$ with quotient digits 0 2 3 6

$30 \div 5 = 6$

$= \underline{236_8}$

** ALL THE DIVISIONS ON THIS PAGE SHOULD **WORK OUT COMPLETELY.** THERE SHOULD NOT BE ANY REMAINDERS IN THE FINAL ANSWERS.

a

Do these divisions in base 6
REMEMBER. Each remainder in the working is **a group of 6**

1) $532_6 \div 4$	*5)* $350_6 \div 3$	*8)* $510_6 \div 3$
2) $1303_6 \div 3$	*6)* $1344_6 \div 2$	*9)* $1512_6 \div 2$
3) $2124_6 \div 4$	*7)* $253_6 \div 5$	*10)* $224_6 \div 4$
4) $221_6 \div 5$		

---

b

Try these divisions in base 8

1) $520_8 \div 4$	*5)* $1452_8 \div 3$	*8)* $3454_8 \div 6$
2) $622_8 \div 6$	*6)* $2104_8 \div 7$	*9)* $473_8 \div 3$
3) $1767_8 \div 5$	*7)* $771_8 \div 5$	*10)* $1674_8 \div 4$
4) $712_8 \div 2$		

---

c

1) $52_6 \div 4$	*6)* $733_8 \div 5$	*11)* $233_5 \div 4$
2) $645_7 \div 3$	*7)* $10021_3 \div 2$	*12)* $664_7 \div 5$
3) $2112_3 \div 2$	*8)* $76_9 \div 3$	*13)* $1210_4 \div 2$
4) $33_5 \div 2$	*9)* $330_4 \div 2$	*14)* $840_9 \div 6$
5) $66_7 \div 4$	*10)* $1034_5 \div 3$	*15)* $2431_6 \div 5$

---

d

1) $2303_5 \div 4$	*6)* $3424_5 \div 3$	*11)* $3652_9 \div 4$
2) $353_6 \div 3$	*7)* $3201_4 \div 3$	*12)* $1102_3 \div 2$
3) $11211_3 \div 2$	*8)* $283_{11} \div 9$	*13)* $3134_8 \div 4$
4) $2651_8 \div 7$	*9)* $2343_7 \div 6$	*14)* $651_{12} \div 5$
5) $132_7 \div 4$	*10)* $623_{10} \div 7$	*15)* $10323_4 \div 3$

---

e

1) $258_9 \div 5$	*6)* $285_9 \times 7$	*11)* $11021_3 - 110_3$
2) $534_7 + 2136_7$	*7)* $1641_7 \div 2$	*12)* $2332_8 \div 6$
3) $234_5 \div 3$	*8)* $6013_8 - 54_8$	*13)* $55_6 \times 5$
4) $1312_4 \times 2$	*9)* $233_4 \times 23_4$	*14)* $331_4 + 23_4 + 302_4$
5) $3210_4 - 323_4$	*10)* $445_6 + 25_6$	*15)* $2412_5 \div 3$

A OTHER BASES (8) — BINARY

BINARY (base 2) can often be easier if you THINK AND COUNT in binary.
Counting in binary goes:
1, 10, 11,100, 101, 110, 111, 1000, 1001, etc.,
so 1 + 1 = 10,   1 + 1 + 1 = 11,   1 + 1 + 1 + 1 = 100, etc.

Addition

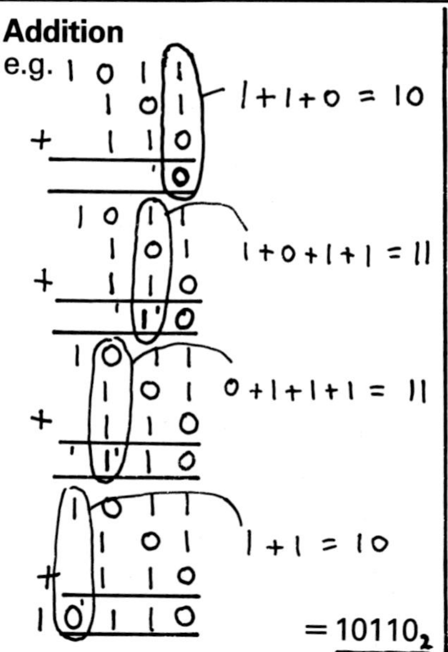

= 10110_2

NOTE. If a column adds up to 100, write 0 and carry **10**.
If a column adds up to 101, write 1 and carry 10, etc.

Subtraction

e.g.

```
  1011 0
-  111
```

0 − 1 is not possible. Borrow 10 from next column
10 − 1 = 1

Same again

There is nothing to borrow, so borrow 10 first from next left column

Then borrow as usual.

```
  10110
-   111
  -----
   1111
```

= 1111_2

Multiplication

e.g. (1)

```
    1110
  ×   11
  ------
    1110
   11100
  ------
  101010
```

1 + 1 = 10, etc.

= 101010_2

e.g. (2)

```
     1101
   ×  101
   ------
     1101
    00000
   110100
  -------
  1000001
```

= 1000001_2

Division

For each piece of working, the answer must be either 1 or 0.

e.g.

```
110)100100
```

```
       1
110)100100
    110
     11
```

```
       110
110)100100
    110
     110
     110
      00
```

= 110_2

** ALL THE NUMBERS IN THESE QUESTIONS ARE IN BINARY (BASE 2)

a

1) $1001 + 10$
2) $111 + 1010$
3) $1101 + 110 + 100$
4) $111 + 111$
5) $10011 + 10111$
6) $1011 + 111 + 10$
7) $11011 + 1101 + 11$
8) $1100 + 110 + 1010$
9) $1010 + 101 + 1110$
10) $1101 + 1100 + 111$

---

b

1) $11110 - 1100$
2) $1110 - 101$
3) $10101 - 1010$
4) $10010 - 100$
5) $1001001 - 10110$
6) $101010 - 1111$
7) $1000 - 101$
8) $110101 - 11000$
9) $1000110 - 1101$
10) $101101 - 11101$

---

c

1) 110×11
2) 1011×10
3) 110×101
4) 1010×111
5) 11001×11
6) 11011×111
7) 10001×101
8) 1101×110
9) 1111×111
10) $1011 \times 101 \times 11$

---

d

1) $11011 \div 11$
2) $10010 \div 11$
3) $1011010 \div 101$
4) $11010 \div 10$
5) $100011 \div 111$
6) $101010 \div 11$
7) $11110 \div 110$
8) $11000 \div 11$
9) $10111001 \div 101$
10) $1000101 \div 11$

---

e

1) $1110 + 111 + 10110$
2) 10101×101
3) $101011 - 1101$
4) 11100×110
5) $100111 \div 11$
6) $10110 - 1011$
7) $101010 + 10101 + 11$
8) $1000010 \div 110$
9) 110111×11
10) $11001 \div 101$
11) $101110 + 11011 + 100110$
12) $110011 - 1010$
13) 101010×111
14) $11000 - 10101$
15) $101111 + 11010 + 1010$

ANGLES (1) - Types and sizes

An ANGLE is the shape made when two straight lines meet at a point. The straight lines are called ARMS of the angle.

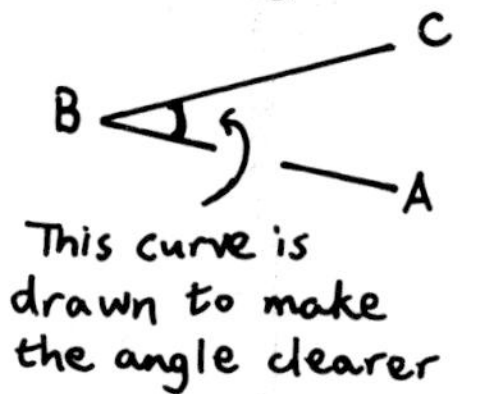

The drawing shows an angle.
This angle can be called ABC or CBA.
Angle ABC can be written in short $A\hat{B}C$. The arms of this angle are AB (or BA) and BC (or CB)

The size of an angle is usually measured in DEGREES (written ° for short).
These angles are marked with their sizes.

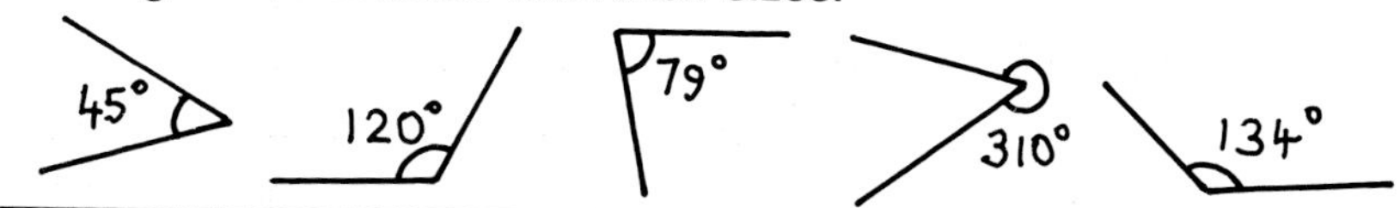

A **RIGHT ANGLE** is a square angle. Its size is 90 degrees (90°). It is usually marked ∟ which means 90 degrees.

A **STRAIGHT ANGLE** is an angle of 180°

A **REVOLUTION** is all the way round. Its size is 360°

An **ACUTE ANGLE** is an angle **more closed up than a right angle.** Its size is less than 90°

e.g.

An **OBTUSE ANGLE** is an angle **wider than a right angle but more closed up than a straight angle.** Its size is more than 90° but less than 180°

e.g.

A **REFLEX ANGLE** is an angle which turns back on itself. Its size is more than 180°.

e.g.

a Using a ruler, make a rough (but larger) copy of each angle. Then complete your copy by naming (a) the angle, and (b) its arms

e.g.

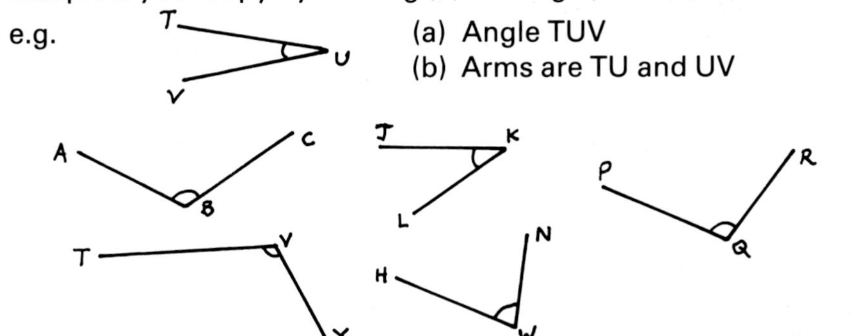

(a) Angle TUV
(b) Arms are TU and UV

---

b Write in short
e.g. Angle ABC = $\hat{ABC}$; 87 degrees = 87°

1) Angle DEF
2) Angle KLM
3) Angle CKG
4) 126 degrees
5) Angle PQR
6) 12 degrees
7) 309 degrees
8) Angle TZP
9) 148 degrees
10) Angle JMC

---

c Using a ruler, make a rough (but larger) copy of each angle. Then complete your copy by writing (a) whether it is ACUTE, RIGHT, OBTUSE, STRAIGHT or REFLEX, and (b) roughly what size you think it is

e.g.

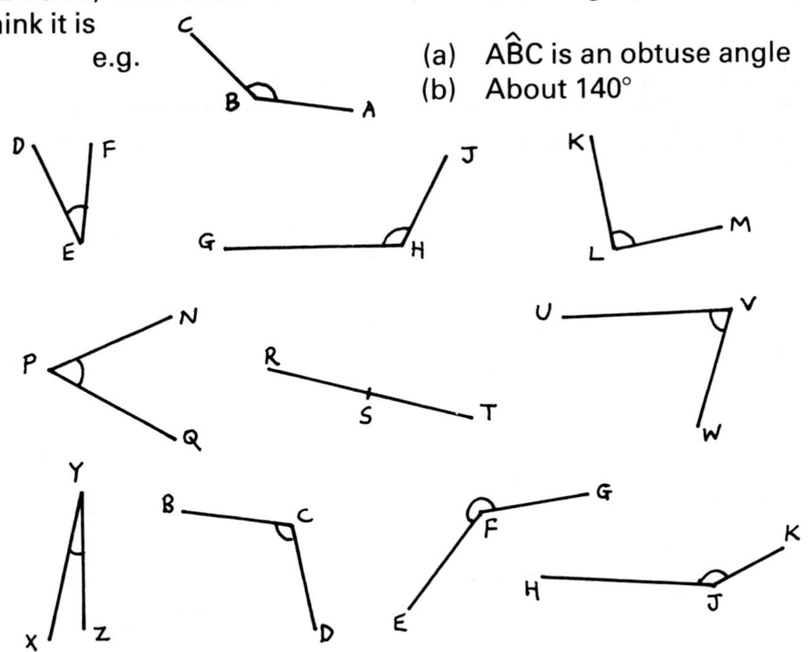

(a) $\hat{ABC}$ is an obtuse angle
(b) About 140°

ANGLES (2) - MEASURING ANGLES

Measuring angles with a protractor

FIRST Make a rough guess. How large is your angle compared with these?

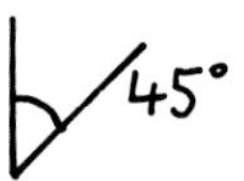

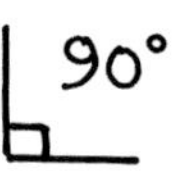

270°

NEXT

*1) Find the **corner** of the angle. If the angle is called a three-letter name (e.g. $A\hat{F}H$), the middle letter is the corner

*2) Place the protractor with the crossing lines on the corner of the angle

*3) Make the 0° line fit along one of the arms of the angle

*4) Look along the other arm of the angle and measure the size on the protractor

*5) **Check with your rough guess** to make sure you have read the angle correctly

---

Clock face

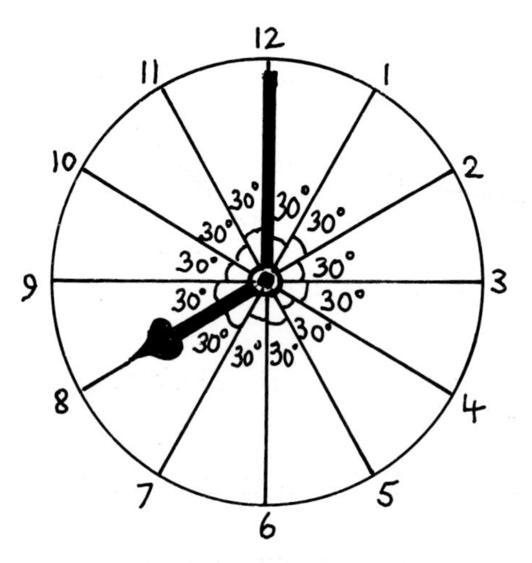

The angle between one number and the next is 30°

e.g. What is the (smaller) angle between the hands of a clock at 8 o'clock?

30 + 30 + 30 + 30

(**or** 4 x 30) = **120°**

The large hand is the **MINUTES** hand.
It moves through **360°** every hour.

The small hand is the **HOURS** hand.
It moves through **30°** every hour.

a Measure each angle and write down its size
e.g. t = 54°, $A\hat{B}C$ = 117°, etc.

If the drawing is too small to measure properly, make an accurate tracing of the angle and extend (or produce) its arms. Then measure your tracing.

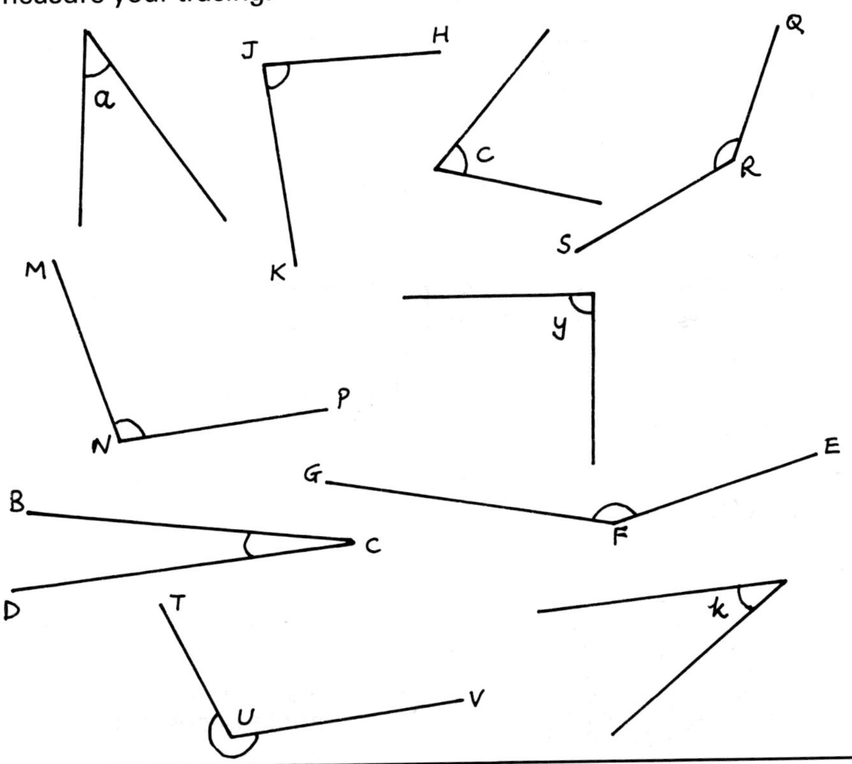

b Find the size of the (smaller) angle between the hands of a clock at

1) 2 o'clock
2) 11 o'clock
3) 5 o'clock
4) 9 o'clock
5) 12 o'clock

c
1) Through what angle does the MINUTES hand move in ½ an hour?
2) Through what angle does the HOURS hand move in ½ hour?

Find the angle between the hands of a clock at

3) 6.30
4) 3.30
5) 7 o'clock
6) 1.30
7) 12.30
8) 4.30
9) 9.30
10) 3.20

A ANGLES (3)

Angles in a REVOLUTION (all the way round a point) add up to 360°

e.g.

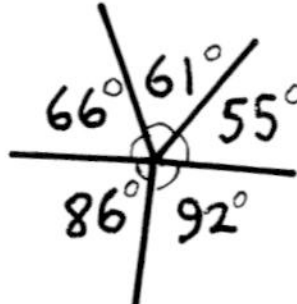

$55 + 92 + 86 + 66 + 61$
$= \mathbf{360°}$

Finding a missing angle

e.g. Find angle k

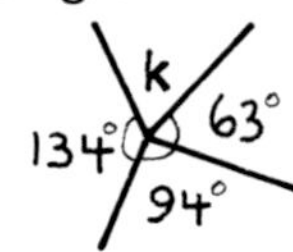

*1) Add all the other angles
$63 + 94 + 134 = 291$
*2) Subtract total from 360
$360 - 291 = 69$ $k = 69°$

e.g. (2) Find angle p

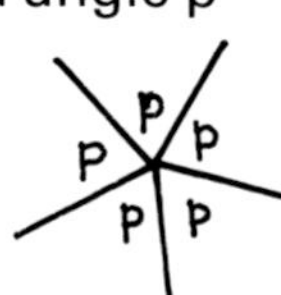

There are 5 angles p, all the same size

$p = \frac{360}{5} = 72$

B

Angles in a QUADRILATERAL add up to 360°
A quadrilateral is a four sided plane figure. Its INTERIOR angles (the angles inside it) add up to 360°

e.g.

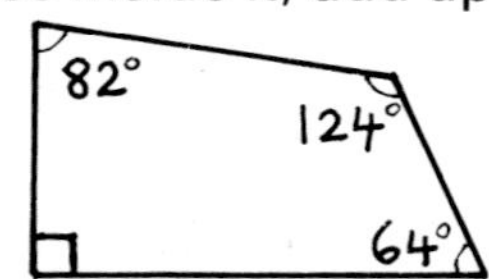

$82 + 64 + 90 + 124 = 360°$

Finding a missing angle

e.g. Find angle JKL

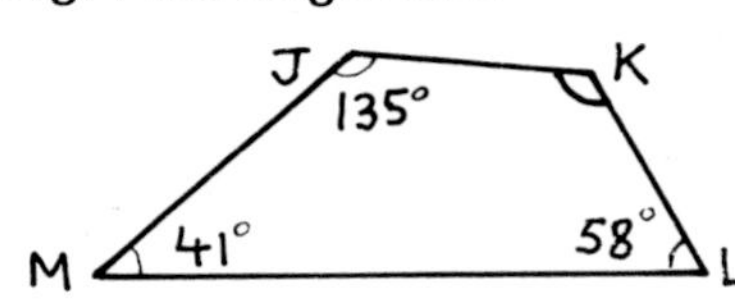

*1) Add all the other angles
$41 + 58 + 135 = 234$
*2) Subtract total from 360
$360 - 234 = 126$
$J\hat{K}L = 126°$

e.g. (2) Find the size of angle w (Both the angles w are the same size)

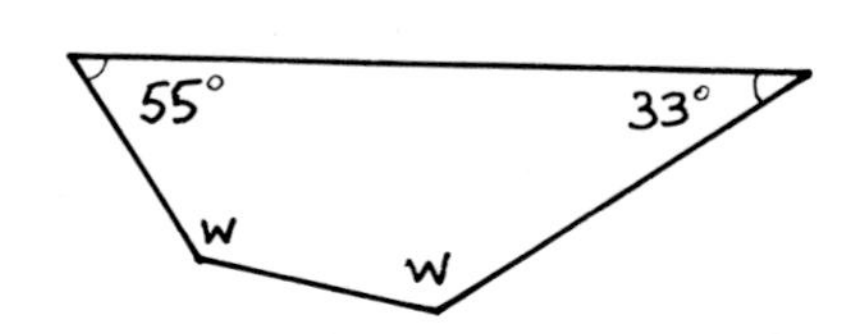

*1) Add the other angles
$55 + 33 = 88$
*2) Subtract total from 360
$360 - 88 = 272$
*3) Divide answer by 2
$w = \frac{272}{2} = 136°$

THESE ANGLES ARE NOT DRAWN TO SCALE. YOUR ANSWERS SHOULD BE **CALCULATED,** NOT MEASURED WITH A PROTRACTOR

a Find the size of each angle a, b, c, d, e

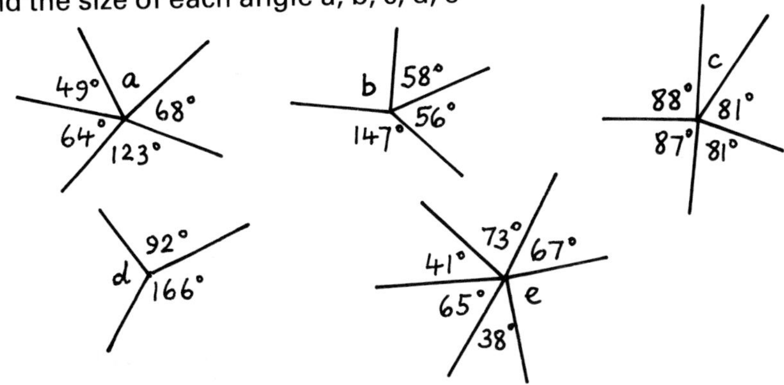

b Find the size of each angle f, g, h, j, k

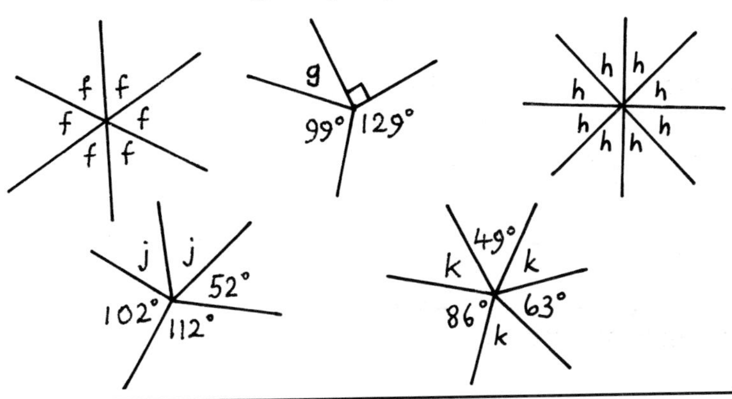

c Find the size of each angle l, m, n, p, q

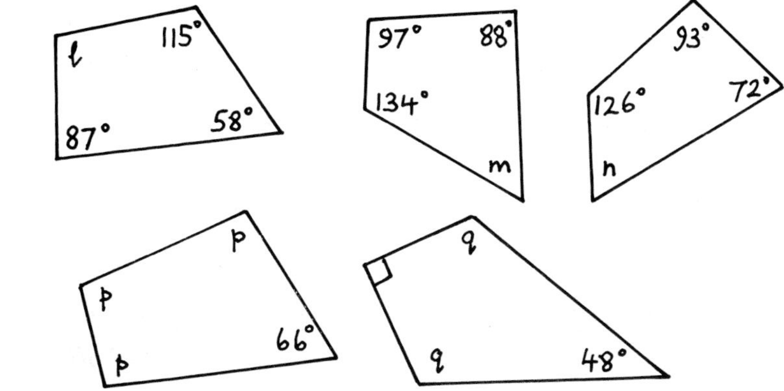

A ANGLES (4)

Angles on a STRAIGHT LINE add up to 180°

e.g.

48 + 132 = 180° 59 + 86 + 35 = 180°

Finding a missing angle

e.g. Find angle QTR

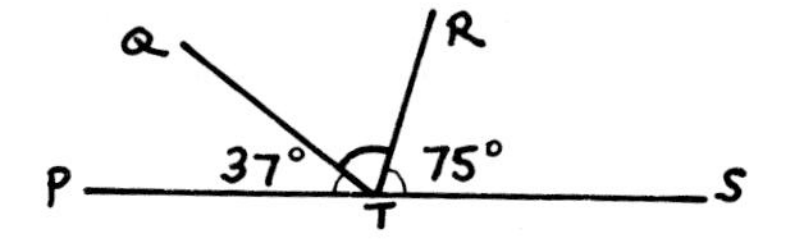

180 − 37 − 75 = 68

$\hat{QTR}$ = 68°

B

Angles in a TRIANGLE add up to 180°

A triangle is a three sided plane figure. Its INTERIOR angles (the angles inside it) add up to 180°

e.g.

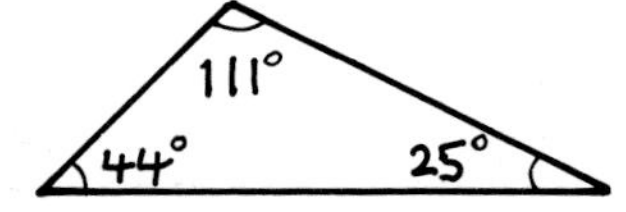

44 + 25 + 111 = 180°

Finding a missing angle

e.g. Calculate $\hat{BCD}$

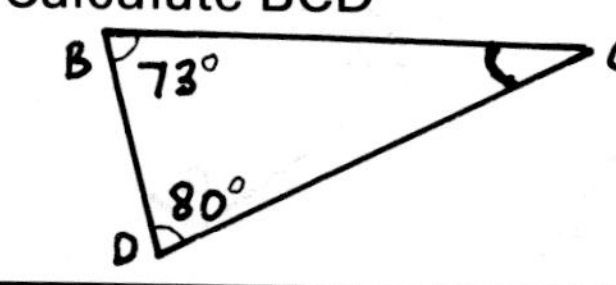

180 − 73 − 80 = 27°

C

ISOSCELES TRIANGLE has two equal angles, and two equal sides

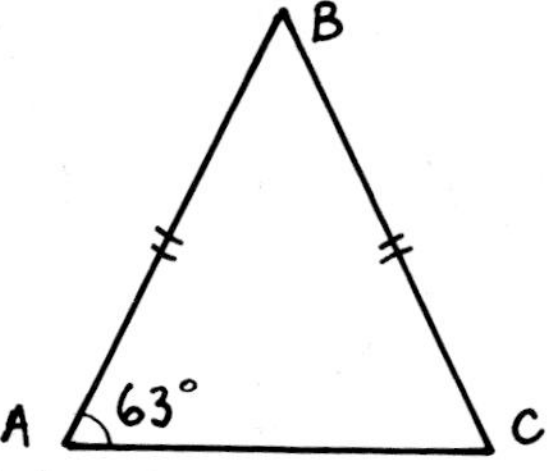

The two sides AB and BC are equal in length. They are marked with the same sort of small lines to show that they are equal.

Angles BAC and BCA are equal

Find the sizes of angles BCA and ABC

1) $\hat{BCA}$ = $\hat{BAC}$ because triangle ABC is isosceles, with AB = BC, so $\hat{BCA}$ = 63°
2) $\hat{ABC}$ = 180 − 63 − 63 = 54°, because angles in a triangle add up to 180°

a

THESE ANGLES ARE NOT DRAWN TO SCALE. YOUR ANSWERS SHOULD BE **CALCULATED,** NOT MEASURED WITH A PROTRACTOR

Find the size of each angle a, b, c, d, e

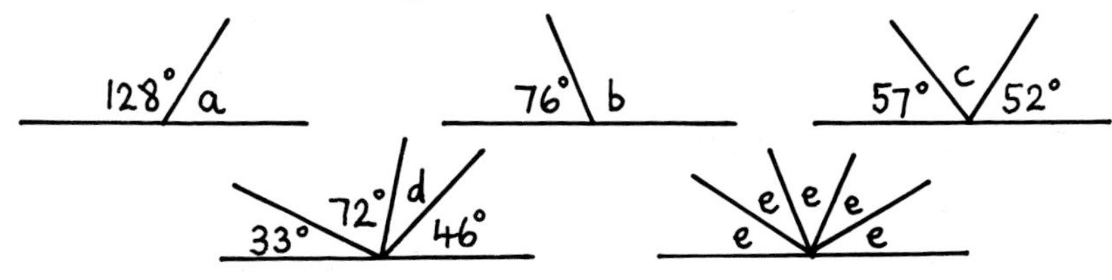

b

Find the size of each angle f, g, h, j, k

f
37°
60°
g
29°
129°
61°
41°
h
70°
j
54°
66°
k
24°

c

Find the size of each angle l, m, n, p, q, r, s, t, u, v

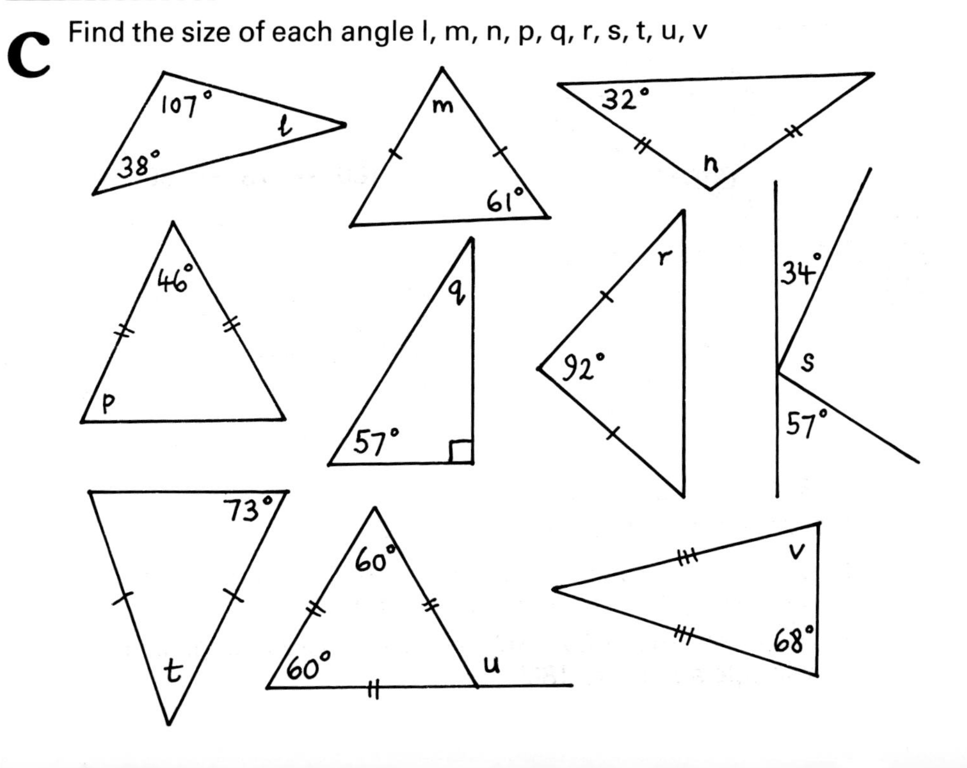

ANGLES (5)

VERTICALLY OPPOSITE ANGLES are equal

Vertically opposite angles are formed at the intersection of two straight lines. Vertically opposite angles are EQUAL

e.g.

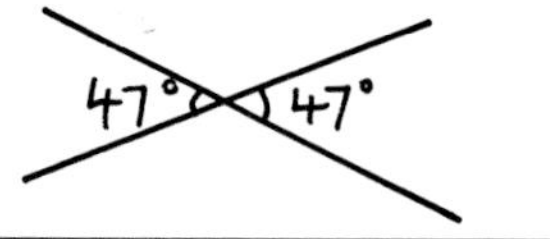

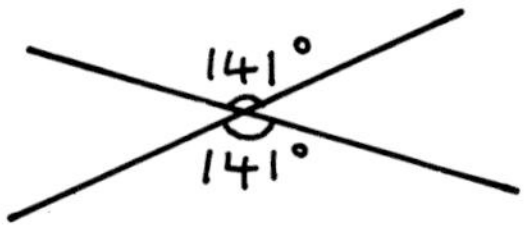

PARALLEL LINES

Parallel lines are pairs or groups of lines which stay the same distance apart.

Parallel lines are marked with the same kind of arrows to show that they are parallel

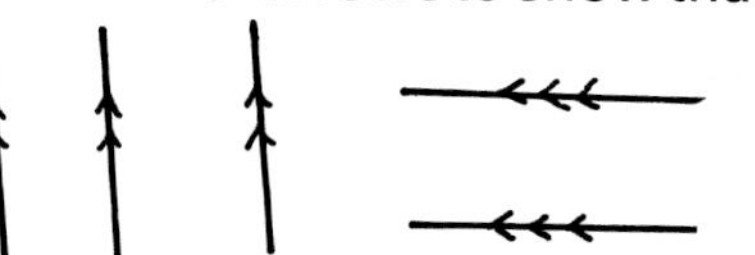

A line which crosses other lines is called a TRANSVERSAL

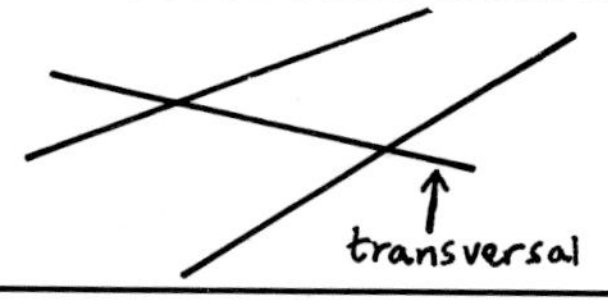

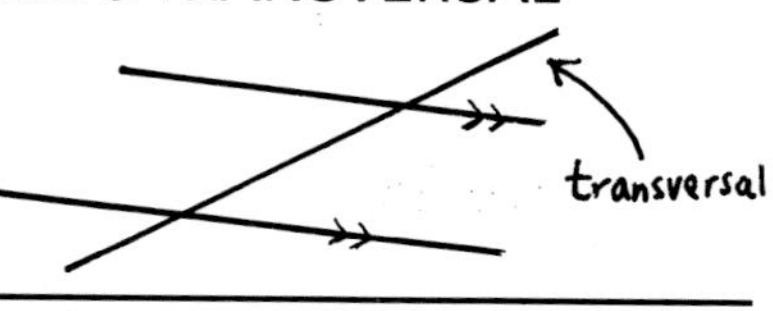

CORRESPONDING ANGLES are equal

Angles in the same position on a set of parallel lines (between a transversal and a set of parallel lines) are called corresponding angles.

Corresponding angles are EQUAL

e.g.

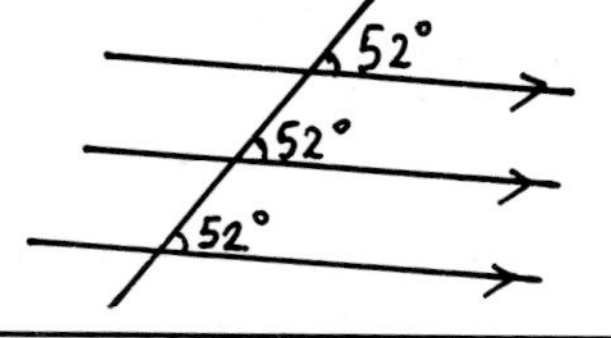

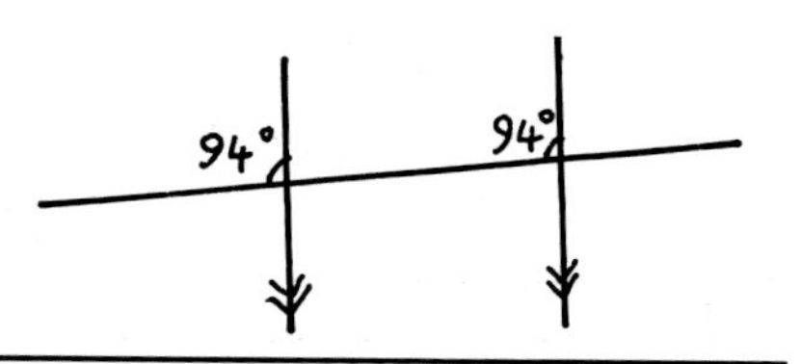

ALTERNATE ANGLES are equal

Angles on two (or more) parallel lines but at opposite sides of the transversal (angles in a Z shape) are called ALTERNATE ANGLES. Alternate angles are EQUAL

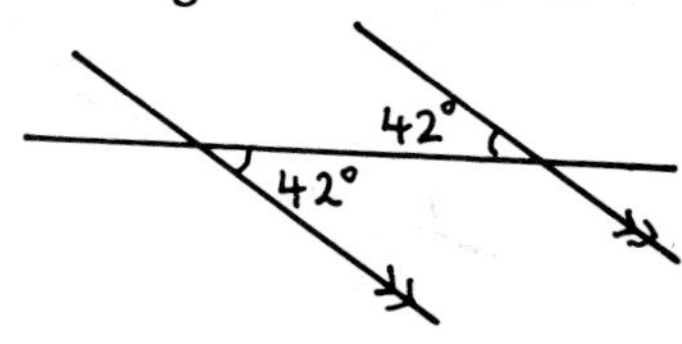

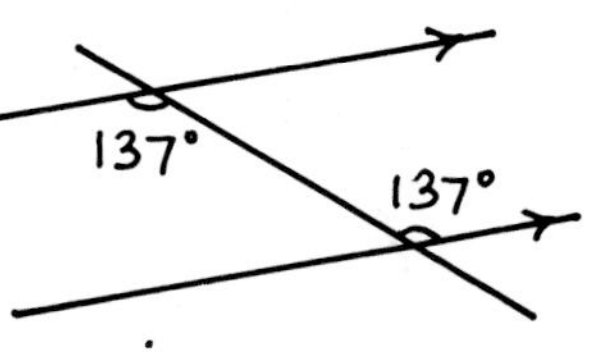

THESE ANGLES ARE NOT DRAWN TO SCALE. YOUR ANSWERS SHOULD BE CALCULATED, NOT MEASURED WITH A PROTRACTOR

a Find the size of each angle, a, b, c, d, e

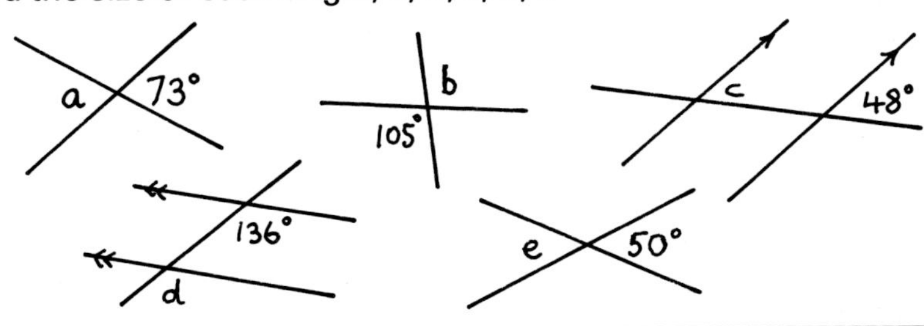

b Find the size of each angle f, g, h, j, k

40°
f
82°
g
h
129°
j
32°
75°
k

c Find the size of each angle l, m, n, p, q, r, s, t, u, v

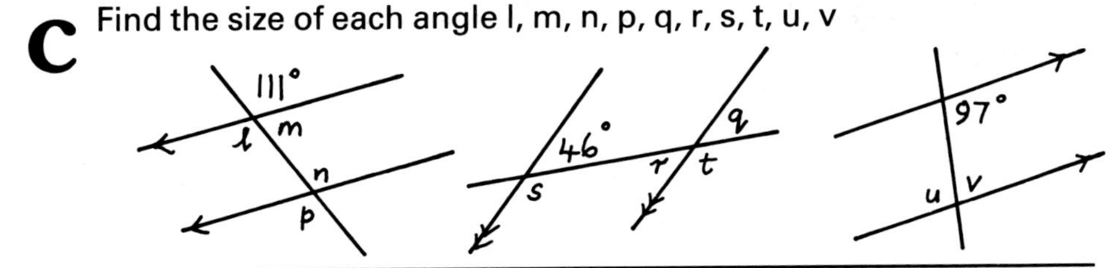

d Find the size of each angle a, b, c, d, e, f, g, h, j, k

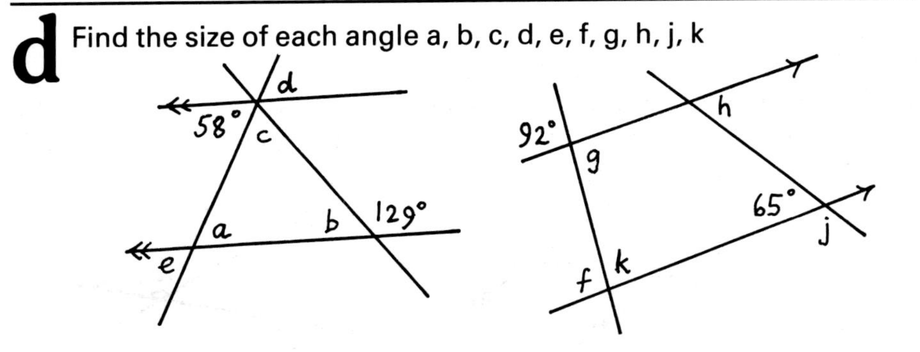

A

ANGLES (6) - 'ANGLE CHASING'

SEVEN RULES TO REMEMBER (see pages 60, 62 and 64)

1) Angles in a REVOLUTION add up to 360°
2) Angles in a QUADRILATERAL add up to 360°
3) Angles on a STRAIGHT LINE add up to 180°
4) Angles in a TRIANGLE add up to 180°
5) VERTICALLY OPPOSITE angles are equal
6) CORRESPONDING angles are equal
7) ALTERNATE angles are equal

It is also useful to remember that an ISOSCELES TRIANGLE has TWO equal sides and TWO equal angles.
Note carefully which two angles are equal

B

Naming an angle

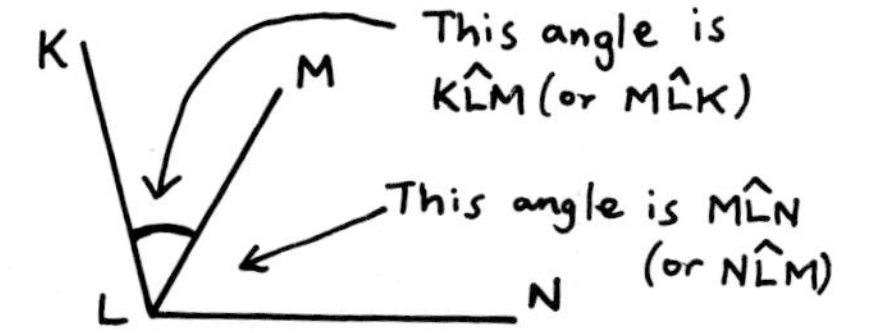

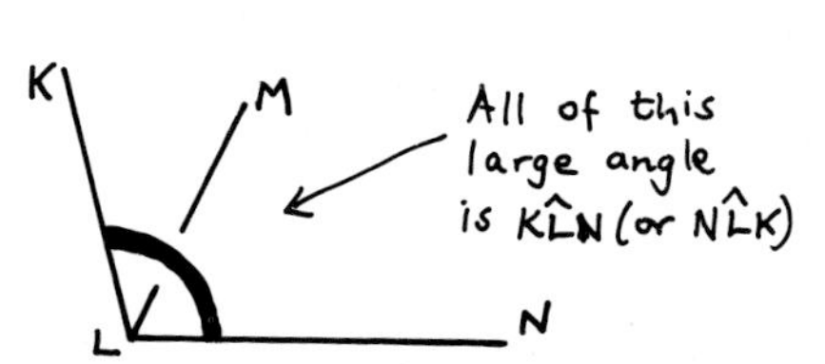

Angle chasing

e.g. Find the sizes of angles (i) GHJ, (ii) GFH and (iii) FGH.

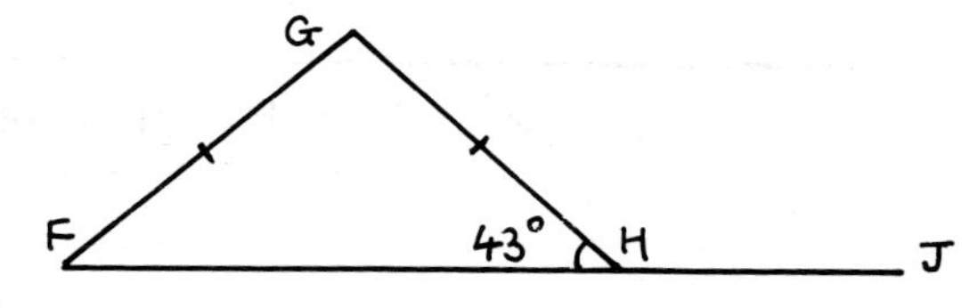

(i) $G\hat{H}F = 43°$

$G\hat{H}J + G\hat{H}F = 180°$ (angles on the straight line FHJ)

so $G\hat{H}J = 180 - 43 = 137°$ $\underline{G\hat{H}J = 137°}$

(ii) $G\hat{F}H = G\hat{H}F$ (GF is the same length as GH, and triangle GFH is isosceles) $\underline{G\hat{F}H = 43°}$

(iii) $F\hat{G}H + G\hat{F}H + G\hat{H}F = 180°$ (angles in triangle GFH add up to 180°)

$F\hat{G}H = 180 - 43 - 43 = 94°$ $\underline{F\hat{G}H = 94°}$

IF IN DIFFICULTY fill in **ANY** angles which you can work out. This may help you to find the one you want.

COPY THE DIAGRAMS ROUGHLY AND FILL IN ON YOUR COPY THE ANGLE SIZES AS YOU FIND THEM

a Find the sizes of angles BDC, ABC and BCD

Write your answer $B\hat{D}C$ =
$A\hat{B}C$ =
$B\hat{C}D$ =

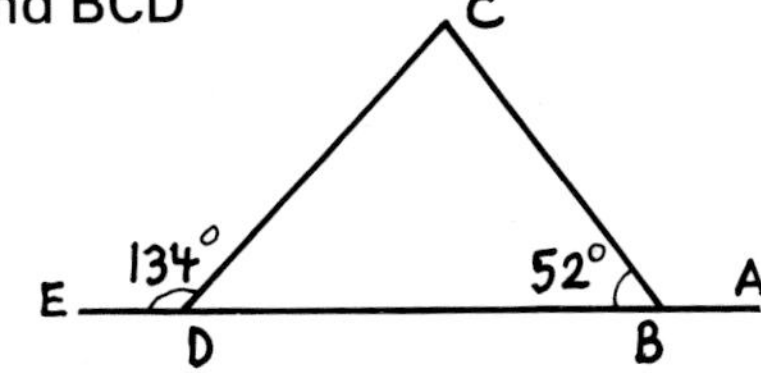

b Find the sizes of $K\hat{M}L$, $K\hat{L}M$, $K\hat{L}R$, $S\hat{M}N$, $L\hat{K}M$ and $P\hat{K}M$

c Calculate the sizes of $C\hat{B}D$, $C\hat{D}B$, $W\hat{D}B$, $D\hat{W}X$ and $C\hat{B}E$.

How do you know that lines CW and XW are equal?

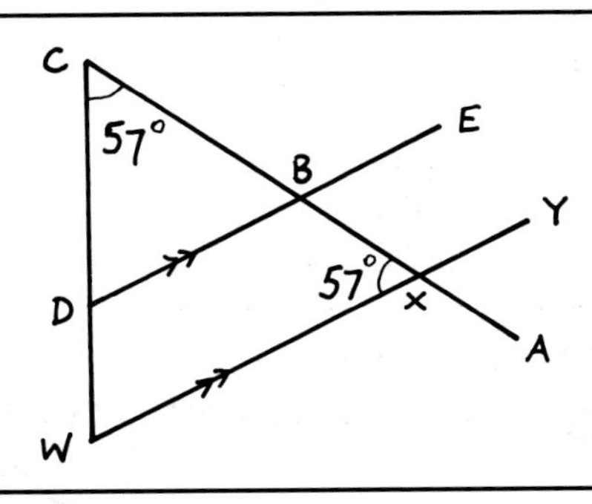

d

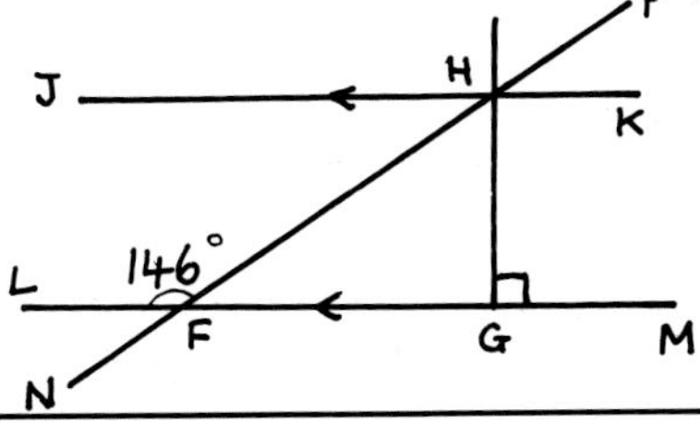

Calculate the sizes of $H\hat{F}G$, $F\hat{G}H$, $J\hat{H}F$, $J\hat{H}P$, $K\hat{H}G$, $K\hat{H}F$ and $P\hat{H}G$.

e PQ = RQ

Calculate the sizes of $A\hat{P}B$, $P\hat{R}Q$, $G\hat{R}P$, $R\hat{P}C$, $Q\hat{P}C$, $P\hat{Q}R$, $R\hat{Q}E$, $H\hat{P}R$, $H\hat{P}Q$ and $C\hat{P}A$

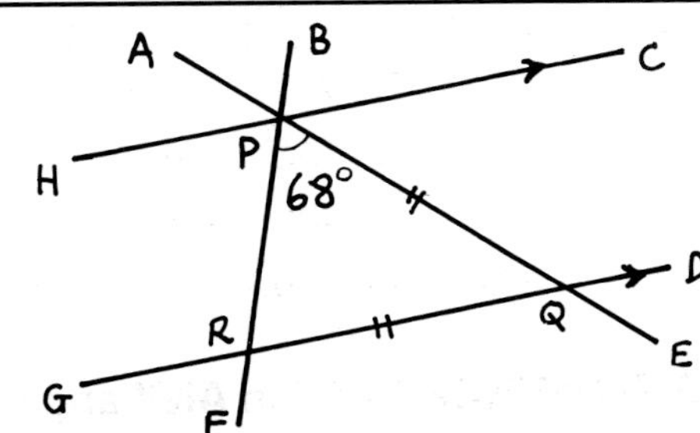

POLYGONS (Many-sided figures)

A POLYGON is a plane figure with 3 or more sides.
A REGULAR POLYGON is a polygon with all its sides the same length and all its angles the same size.

5 sided figure is a PENTAGON	8 sided figure is an OCTAGON
6 sided figure is a HEXAGON	9 sided figure is a NONAGON
7 sided figure is a HEPTAGON	10 sided figure is a DECAGON

EXTERIOR ANGLES of any polygon add up to 360°
e.g.

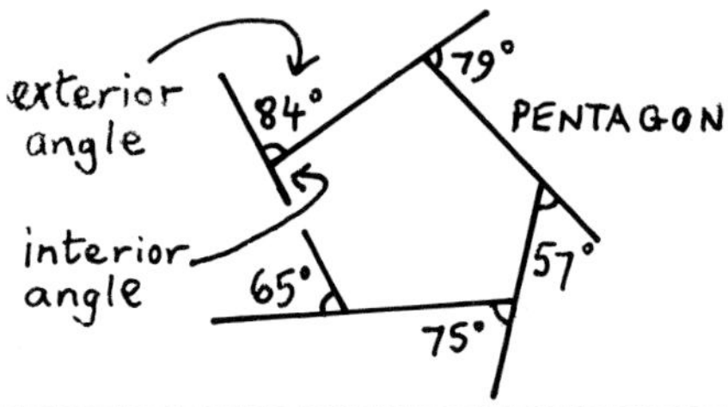

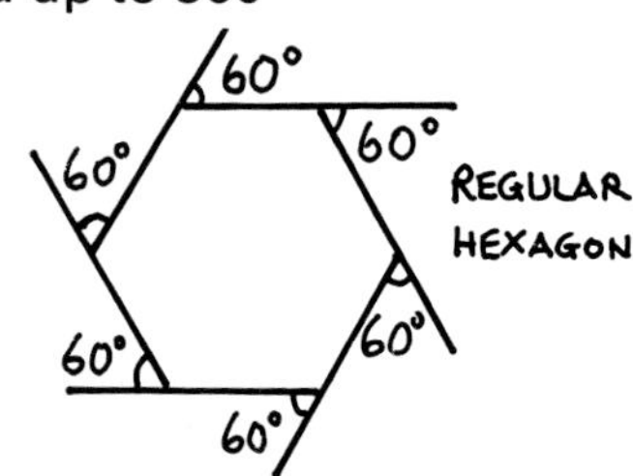

INTERIOR ANGLES

To find the size of **each interior angle** of a regular polygon

e.g. Find each interior angle of a regular 6 sided figure

*1) Find each EXterior angle by dividing 360° by the number of angles $\frac{360}{6} = 60°$

*2) Subtract from 180° $180 - 60 = 120°$

To find the sum (total) of interior angles of a regular polygon, multiply **each interior angle** by the **number of angles**

e.g. in a 6 sided figure $120 \times 6 = 720°$

FORMULA for finding SUM OF INTERIOR ANGLES
of an N-sided polygon

$$S = 180\ (N - 2) \text{ degrees}$$

e.g. Sum of interior angles of a 9 sided figure

$$= 180\,(9 - 2) = 180 \times 7 = 1260°$$

To find the number of sides (N) from the sum (S) of interior angles

$$N = \frac{S}{180} + 2$$

e.g. How many sides has a polygon whose interior angles add up to 1980°?

$$N = \frac{1980}{180} + 2 = 13 \text{ sides}$$

a

Find the size of each **exterior** angle of

1) a regular pentagon
2) a regular octagon
3) a regular 12 sided figure
4) a regular 20 sided figure
5) a regular nonagon
6) a regular decagon
7) a regular 36 sided figure
8) a regular (square) quadrilateral
9) a regular 16 sided figure
10) a regular (equilateral) triangle

b

Find the size of each **interior** angle of

1) a regular octagon
2) a regular 15 sided figure
3) a regular hexagon
4) a regular quadrilateral
5) a regular 30 sided figure
6) a regular 12 sided figure
7) a regular pentagon
8) a regular 24 sided figure
9) a regular decagon
10) a regular nonagon

c

Find the **sum** of the interior angles of

1) a decagon
2) a heptagon
3) a 20 sided figure
4) a triangle
5) pentagon
6) a 14 sided figure
7) a 22 sided figure
8) a quadrilateral
9) an 11 sided figure
10) a 17 sided figure

d

Find the number of sides of the polygon whose interior angles add up to

1) 720°
2) 2340°
3) 1080°
4) 1800°
5) 1260°

e

1) The sum of the interior angles of a polygon is 2520°. How many sides has the polygon?
2) Four of the interior angles of a pentagon have sizes 96°, 104°, 117° and 150°. Find the size of the other interior angle
3) Each exterior angle of a certain regular polygon is 24°. How many sides has the polygon?
4) Each interior angle of a certain regular polygon is 160°. How many sides has the polygon?
5) Four of the interior angles of a hexagon are 105°, 109°, 134° and 138°. The other two angles are equal. What size is each of the missing angles?

SOME EXTRA QUESTIONS

1) Write in 24 hour clock notation (a) 8.50 p.m. (b) 12.18 a.m. (c) 1.47 p.m.

2) Calculate the sizes of angles v and w (not drawn to scale)

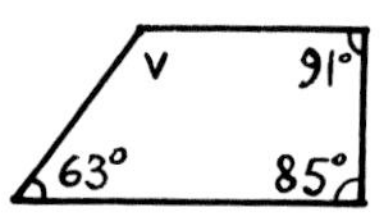

3) Find the union of each of these pairs of sets

(a) $\{\frac{1}{2}, \frac{1}{4}, \frac{1}{3}, \frac{1}{5}, \frac{1}{6}\}$, $\{\frac{1}{6}, \frac{1}{3}, \frac{1}{2}, \frac{2}{3}, \frac{5}{6}\}$

(b) {○, ◐, ⊖, ●}, {◑, ⊕, ◒}

4) (a) $307_9 + 58_9 + 461_9$ (b) $2163_8 - 707_8$

5) A train travelled from Stoke-on-Trent to London, a distance of 150 miles, at an average speed of 72 miles/hour. How long, in hours and minutes, did its journey take?

6) Find the size of (a) each exterior (b) each interior, angle of a regular 18 sided figure

7) Find the average of 16, 23, 18, 20, 15, 17, 22 and 21

8) Copy the questions and complete them with the correct answers

$D \cap C =$ .... $n(C) =$ ....

$D \cup C =$ .... $(D \cup C)' =$ ....

$C' =$ ....

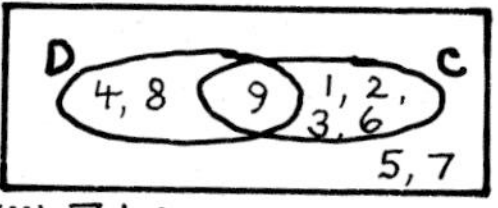

9) Write as a number of minutes (i) $\frac{11}{15}$ hour, (ii) $7\frac{1}{2}$ hours (iii) $\frac{5}{12}$ hour

10)

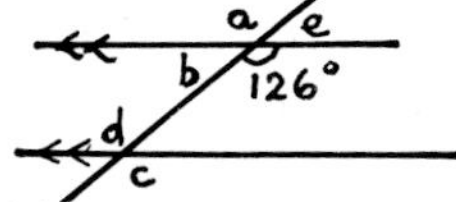

Calculate the sizes of angles a,b,c,d and e (not drawn to scale)

11) (a) Add 1 hour 55 min, 2 hours 23 min, 2 hours 48 min

(b) Multiply 5 hours 27 minutes by 4

12) (i) Find the next eight consecutive numbers above 21 in base 3

(ii) Find the next three consecutive numbers below 101 in base 5

13) Draw a Venn diagram to show ℰ = {a, b, c, d, e, f, g}

W = {b, c, d}, Z = {c, d, e, f}

14) Make a rough larger copy of each of these angles and write what kind each angle is (e.g. acute angle)

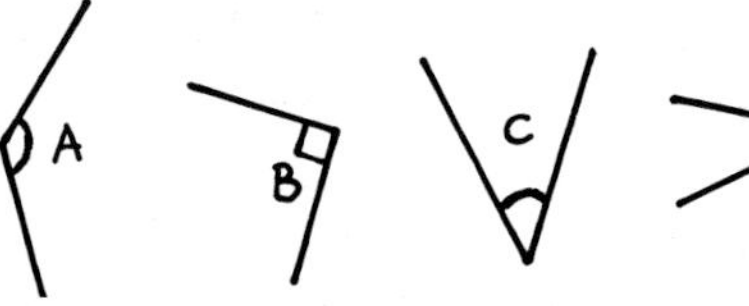

15) (a) $11101_2 \times 101_2$ (b) $1101101_2 - 10110_2$

16) Express as a fraction of an hour in its lowest terms

(i) 21 minutes (ii) 6 minutes (iii) 56 minutes

17) Find (a) the H.C.F. and (b) the L.C.M. of 198 and 108. Draw a Venn diagram to show the prime factors

18) A length of motorway began to be built in November 1984 and was finished 2 years 5 months later. In which month of which year was it finished?

19) Write (a) 1222_3 in denary (b) 327_{10} in base 6

20) Calculate the speed (S) from each distance (D) and time (T)
(i) D = 750 miles, T = 12 hours
(ii) D = 23.4 metres, T = 1.8 seconds

21) 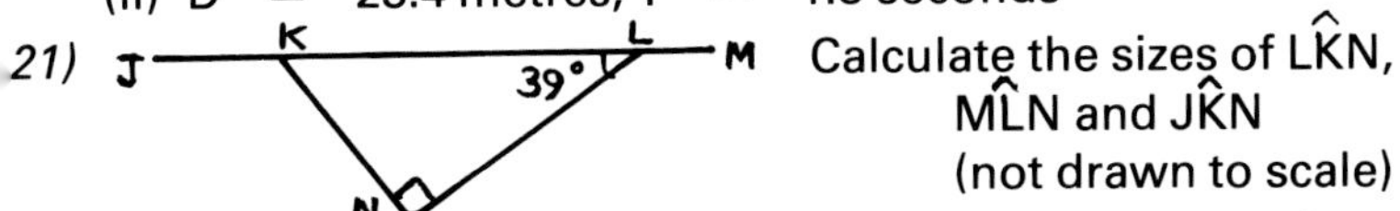

Calculate the sizes of $L\hat{K}N$, $M\hat{L}N$ and $J\hat{K}N$ (not drawn to scale)

22) Write in short, using the correct sign instead of each group of underlined words
(a) moth is a member of the set of insects
(b) G is a subset of M
(c) A = an empty set, so the number of members of A = 0

23) (i) Express 15 metres/second in km/hour
(ii) Express 810 km/hour in metres/second

24) A bus set off at 1445 and travelled for 3 hours 38 minutes. At what time did it complete its journey?

25) (a) $431_5 \times 42_5$ (b) $223_4 + 303_4 + 321_4$

26) For each of these groups of sets, draw the best possible Venn diagram and write each number in its correct region
(i) A = {32, 22, 16, 11, 8}, B = {2.8, 4, 5.6, 8, 11}
(ii) $\mathscr{E}$ = {1,2,3,4,5,6,7,8,9}, G = {3,6,9}, H = {1,2,4,8}

27) (a) Subtract 5 years 9 months from 10 years 7 months
(b) Divide 14 years 8 months by 4

28) Find the average of $\frac{3}{4}$, $\frac{5}{8}$, $\frac{7}{24}$ and $\frac{2}{3}$

29) By converting TO DENARY first, express 263_7 as a number in base 3

30) What is the sum of the interior angles of
(i) a 12 sided figure? (ii) a 19 sided figure?

31) A car travelled for 3 hours 40 minutes at an average speed of 42 miles/hour. How far did it travel?

32) Draw a copy of this Venn diagram. Write the correct number of members in each region

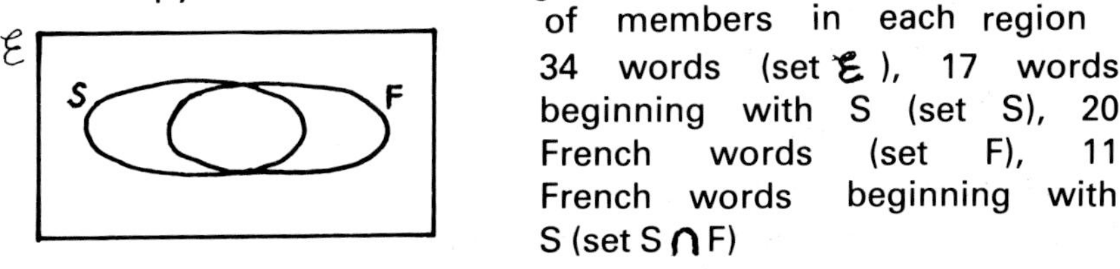

34 words (set $\mathscr{E}$), 17 words beginning with S (set S), 20 French words (set F), 11 French words beginning with S (set $S \cap F$)

33) (a) Add in binary 11010_2, 101110_2, and 1101_2
(b) Divide 111001_2 by 11_2

34) Write in a.m. or p.m. notation (a) 0245, (b) 2121, (c) 1207

35) Calculate the sizes of angles G and H (not drawn to scale)

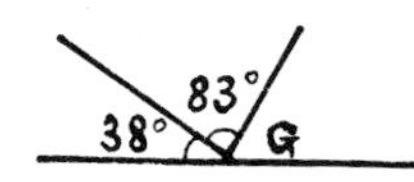

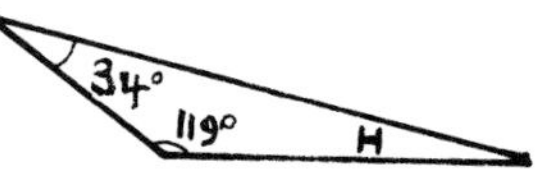

36) Write down the first sixteen numbers in base 4, starting with 1

37) For each of these pairs of sets, draw a Venn diagram showing the subset inside the larger set
(a) {P, Q, R, S, T, V}, {P,R,V}
(b) {27, 30}, {26, 27, 28, 29, 30, 31, 32}

38) Express as hours and fractions of an hour
(i) 2 hours 27 minutes (ii) 8 hours 36 minutes

39) (a) $345_6 \times 43_6$ (b) $1425_7 \div 6$

40) Find the angle between the hands of a clock at
(a) 4 o'clock (b) 7.30 (c) 2.10

41) Make a larger copy of this Venn diagram. Write the correct NUMBER of members in each region.
$\mathcal{E}$ = {animals}, L = {large animals}, B = {brown animals}, F = {furry animals}

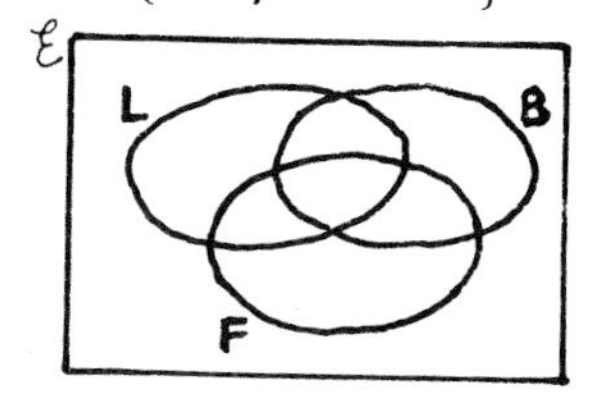

70 animals altogether; 11 large brown furry animals; 8 large furry animals which are not brown; 15 brown furry animals which are not large; 40 furry animals altogether; 7 large animals which are not brown and not furry; 35 large animals altogether; 10 animals which are not large, not brown and not furry

42) Express 61_{10} in (a) binary (b) octal

43) The average mass of six boys was 42kg. The masses of five of the boys were 53kg, 46kg, 44kg, 37kg and 34kg. What was the mass of the other boy?

44)

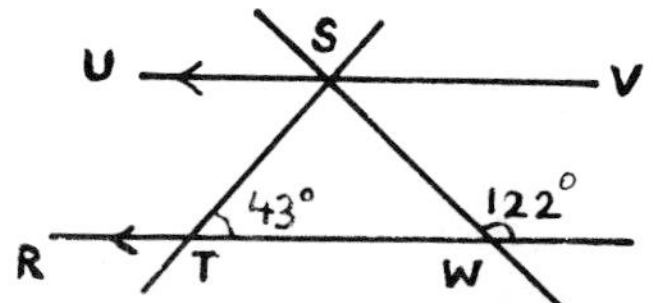

Calculate the sizes of $S\hat{W}T$, $V\hat{S}W$, $R\hat{T}S$, $U\hat{S}T$ and $T\hat{S}W$ (not drawn to scale)

45) David ran 1500 metres in exactly 6 minutes. Calculate his speed in metres/second.

46) Make a list of **all** the subsets of {j, k, l, m}

47) Convert (a) 922_{10} to base 9 (b) 465_7 to denary

48) Four of the angles in a heptagon are 93°, 105°, 144° and 159°. The other three angles are equal. What size is each of the other angles?

49) If J = {2, 5, 8, 11, 14}, K = {2, 3, 5, 7, 11, 13},
find (i) $J \cap K$, (ii) $J \cup K$, (iii) n(K)

50) An aeroplane took off from Dallas at 2235 and flew 632 miles to Denver to an average speed of 237 miles/hour. At what time did it arrive in Denver?

FOR PRACTICE

Ashish Mandavia
4 Burnside Close
Twickenham
Middlesex TW1 1ET
Tel: 0181 891 0495

5

MATRICES

VECTORS

SIMULTANEOUS AND
QUADRATIC EQUATIONS

TRIGONOMETRY

CIRCLES

PETER ROBSON

PO BOX 40, SCARBOROUGH
NORTH YORKSHIRE, YO12 5TW
TEL/FAX 01723 362713

SQUARE ROOTS

Finding the square root (√) of a number

If a number is not a perfect square (integer X itself) the square root will not work out exactly.

Square roots to an accuracy of 3 significant figures can be worked out using the table in the back of this book.
For greater accuracy, use an electronic calculator with a √ button.

The examples on this page are worked out to 3 significant figures.

e.g. (1) Calculate the square root of 5000

*If the number is between 1 and 100 (inclusive), simply look up in the table. Otherwise, change the number by dividing or multiplying by 100 until you have a new number between 1 and 100 — $5000 \div \mathbf{100} = 50$

*Look up the square root of your new number — $\sqrt{50} = 7.07$

*Multiply or divide your square root by 10 the correct number of times — $7.07 \times \mathbf{10} = 70.7$

Answer $\sqrt{5000} = 70.7$

---

e.g. (2) Find the value of $\sqrt{83000}$

$83000 \div \mathbf{100} \div \mathbf{100} = 8.3$

$\sqrt{8.3} = 2.88$

$\sqrt{83000} = 2.88 \times \mathbf{10} \times \mathbf{10} = 288$

---

e.g. (3) Find the square root of 0.09

$0.09 \times \mathbf{100} = 9$

$\sqrt{9} = 3$

$\sqrt{0.09} = 3 \div \mathbf{10} = 0.3$

---

e.g. (4) Find, to 3 sig. figs., the square root of 0.0059

$0.0059 \times \mathbf{100} \times \mathbf{100} = 59$

$\sqrt{59} = 7.68$

$\sqrt{0.0059} = 7.68 \div \mathbf{10} \div \mathbf{10}$

$= 0.0768$

NOTE Square roots can be worked out by trial and error (even on a desert island without a calculator) if you remember some rough guidelines: $\sqrt{1} = 1$, $\sqrt{4} = 2$, $\sqrt{9} = 3$, $\sqrt{16} = 4$, $\sqrt{25} = 5$, $\sqrt{36} = 6$, $\sqrt{49} = 7$, etc., e.g. $\sqrt{38}$ must be between 6 and 7, so try 6.1 x 6.1, etc.

a Look up, in the table on page 71, the square roots of these numbers

1) 17	4) 41	7) 1.3	10) 67	13) 50
2) 75	5) 5.9	8) 9.0	11) 6.7	14) 5.0
3) 3.4	6) 86	9) 22	12) 15	15) 7.7

---

b Find the square root of each of these numbers

1) 230	6) 1400	11) 18000
2) 8300	7) 0.69	12) 35
3) 57000	8) 650	13) 0.42
4) 2.8	9) 0.088	14) 7100
5) 0.028	10) 0.0088	15) 0.054

---

c Find the value of each of these

1) $\sqrt{0.33}$	6) $\sqrt{1000}$	11) $\sqrt{0.085}$
2) $\sqrt{68}$	7) $\sqrt{1.8}$	12) $\sqrt{620}$
3) $\sqrt{45000}$	8) $\sqrt{0.0052}$	13) $\sqrt{0.00023}$
4) $\sqrt{0.092}$	9) $\sqrt{490}$	14) $\sqrt{1900000}$
5) $\sqrt{390000}$	10) $\sqrt{4900}$	15) $\sqrt{0.74}$

---

d Using the table on page 71, estimate the square root of each of these numbers

1) 78.5	6) 3.35	11) 11.5
2) 26.5	7) 63.5	12) 4.45
3) 2.05	8) 9.25	13) 46.5
4) 82.5	9) 1.35	14) 6.85
5) 7.75	10) 55.5	15) 1.25

---

e Find the **square** of each of these numbers

1) 15 2) 41 3) 24 4) 9 5) 67

From your answers to questions 1, 2, 3, 4 and 5 (but not in that order), write down the exact square root of

6) 8100	8) 448900	10) 0.0576
7) 16.81	9) 2.25	

A PYTHAGORAS' THEOREM

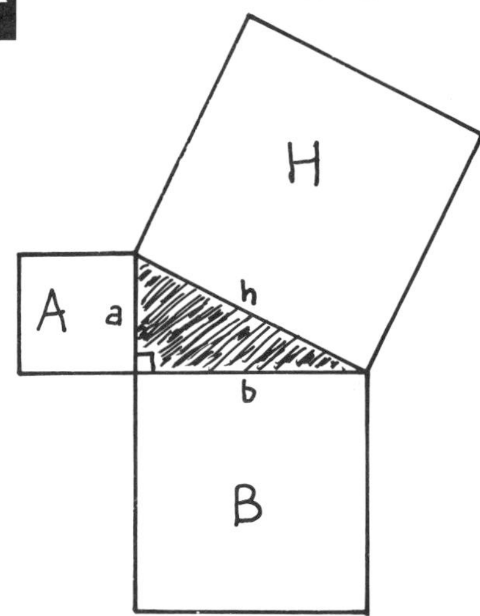

In a right-angled triangle, the square on the hypotenuse is equal to the sum of the squares on the other two sides.

NOTE. The hypotenuse is the longest side of a right-angled triangle (i.e. the side opposite the right angle)

In the diagram
area H = area A + area B
or $h^2 = a^2 + b^2$

e.g. (1) Find the length of h if a = 3cm, b = 4cm

$h^2 = 3^2 + 4^2$
$h^2 = 9 + 16$
$h^2 = 25$
$h = \sqrt{25}$
$h = 5$ Length of h is 5cm

e.g. (2) Find the length, correct to 1 decimal place, of the hypotenuse of a triangle whose other two sides are 11cm and 19cm

$h^2 = 11^2 + 19^2$
$h^2 = 121 + 361$
$h^2 = 482$
$h = \sqrt{482}$
$h = 22.0$ cm (1 d.p.)

e.g. (3) Find the length b, correct to 1 decimal place, if h = 23m and a = 20m

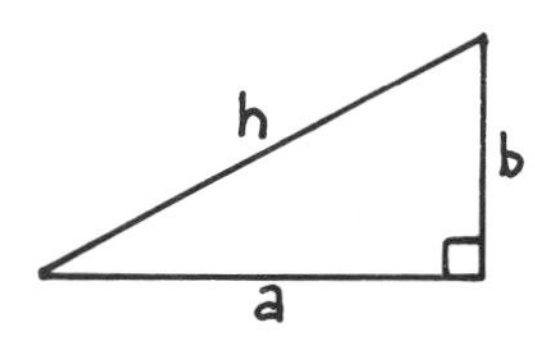

$h^2 = a^2 + b^2$
$b^2 = h^2 - a^2$
$b^2 = 529 - 400$
$b^2 = 129$
$b = \sqrt{129} = 11.4$m (1 d.p.)

a

Find the length of the hypotenuse (h) in each triangle. If the square root does not work out exactly (questions 11 to 20) give your answer correct to 1 decimal place

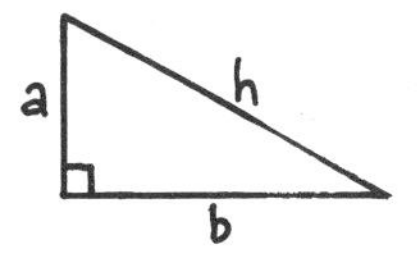

1) a = 8, b = 6
2) a = 7, b = 24
3) a = 8, b = 15
4) a = 16, b = 12
5) a = 9, b = 40
6) a = 0.5, b = 1.2
7) a = 9, b = 12
8) a = 80, b = 18
9) a = 1, b = $\frac{3}{4}$
10) a = 63, b = 16
11) a = 9, b = 6
12) a = 5, b = 5
13) a = 2, b = 4
14) a = 8, b = 3
15) a = 7, b = 11
16) a = 1.5, b = 3.8
17) a = 14, b = 6.5
18) a = 10, b = 9
19) a = 2.7, b = 7.2
20) a = 20, b = 12

b

Find the length of a in each triangle (like the one at the top of the page). If the square root does not work out exactly (questions 11 to 15) give your answer correct to 1 decimal place.

1) h = 26, b = 10
2) h = 61, b = 60
3) h = 25, b = 20
4) h = 7.5, b = 2.1
5) h = 39, b = 36
6) h = $2\frac{1}{6}$, b = $\frac{5}{6}$
7) b = 80, h = 100
8) h = 221, b = 21
9) h = 0.05, b = 0.04
10) b = 30, h = 34
11) h = 10, b = 5
12) h = 43, b = 27
13) h = 6, b = 4.5
14) b = 19, h = 22
15) h = 3.4, b = 0.8

c

1) Tebsworth is 9 miles due north of Petersby; Dalton is 12 miles due east of Petersby. How far is Tebsworth from Dalton?

2) A ladder is placed with its foot on level ground 4 m from a vertical wall. The top of the ladder is 7.5 m up the wall. Find the length of the ladder.

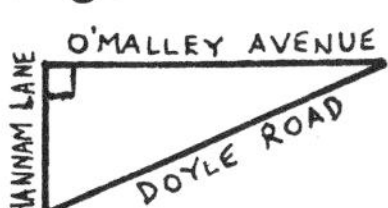

3) In the drawing on the left, Doyle Road is 650 m long and O'Malley Avenue is 630 m long. How long is Hannam Lane?

T
W
B

4) In the drawing on the right, a vertical flagpole (TB) 10 m high is secured by a wire (TW) 12.5 m long. How far is the bottom of the wire from the foot of the flagpole?

5)

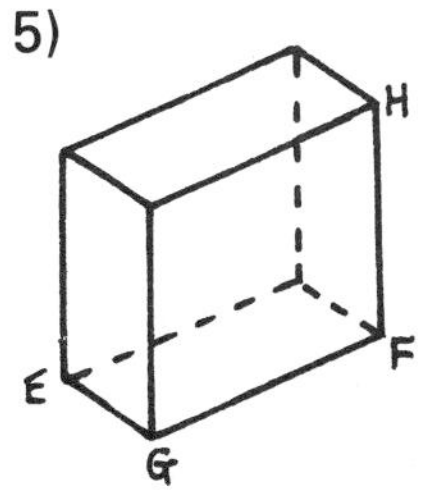

The drawing shows a box in the shape of a cuboid 48 cm long (GF), 36 cm wide (EG), 25 cm high (FH).

(a) By studying triangle EFG, work out the length EF

(b) From your answer to part (a) and by studying triangle EFH, work out the length EH

SIMULTANEOUS EQUATIONS(1)

To solve simultaneous equations, the values of two (or more) different letters must be found.

e.g. Solve the simultaneous equations

$$x + y = 8$$
$$x - y = 2$$

Answer $\begin{cases} x = 5 \\ y = 3 \end{cases}$

because $5 + 3 = 8$
$5 - 3 = 2$

The answer to simultaneous equations is written with a curly bracket

$$\begin{cases} x = \\ y = \end{cases}$$

There are several different ways of solving simultaneous equations, including

1) substitution
2) elimination (see page 8 A)
3) drawing graphs (see page 10 A)
4) using matrices (see page 20 C)

Substitution

e.g. Solve the simultaneous equations $x + y = 12$, $2x - y = 9$

$x + y = 12$ ....equation ①
$2x - y = 9$ ....equation ②

*Rearrange equation ① to give the value of y in terms of x

$$y = 12 - x$$

*Now, using this value of y, substitute for y in equation ②

$$2x - (12 - x) = 9$$

*Solve for x

$$2x - 12 + x = 9$$
$$3x = 21$$
$$x = 7$$

*Find the value of y by substituting in equation ①

$7 + y = 12$, so the answer is $\begin{cases} x = 7 \\ y = 5 \end{cases}$

*NOTE. For the first stage, always choose the easier of the two equations. It does not matter which letter value is found first.

a

Solve these simultaneous equations by substitution

1) $x + y = 10$, $x - y = 6$
2) $a + b = 7$, $2a - b = 5$
3) $3j + h = 29$, $j - h = 3$
4) $m + 2p = 17$, $m + p = 12$
5) $x - y = 1$, $3y - 2x = 8$
6) $d + e = 13$, $2d - 4e = 20$
7) $4q + p = 13$, $p - q = 3$
8) $2d - c = 8$, $c - d = 1$
9) $2v + w = 7$, $2w + v = 8$
10) $3a - c = 3$, $c - a = 5$
11) $k - m = 2$, $3m - k = 6$
12) $2x + y = 5$, $x - y = 1$
13) $2t - s = 12$, $2s + t = 6$
14) $g - e = -1$, $e + g = 5$
15) $a - 3k = -5$, $k - a = -3$

---

b

Solve these simultaneous equations

1) $w + 3u = 2$, $u - w = 6$
2) $x + y = 3$, $x - y = 9$
3) $m + 2j = 3$, $j + 2m = 9$
4) $e - d = 2$, $2d - e = 2$
5) $z + y = 6$, $2z - y = 18$
6) $t - u = 2$, $3t + u = 2$
7) $4b - 2a = -6$, $a - b = 1$
8) $3f - g = 12$, $f + 3g = -6$
9) $p - q = -1$, $2q - p = 6$
10) $x + y = -7$, $5y - 4x = 1$
11) $4c + d = 4$, $d - 2c = 1$
12) $m + 5n = 4$, $2n - 6m = 8$
13) $4x - y = 6$, $y + 2x = 9$
14) $2q - 3s = -14$, $q - s = 2$
15) $2h + t = 2$, $2t + 6h = 1$

---

c

Solve for x and y in each of these by substitution

1) $y = x + 2$, $3x + 1 = 2y$
2) $y = 2x + 6$, $x + y = 3$
3) $x - 3y = 2$, $y = \frac{1}{4}x + 2$
4) $y = 2x - 5$, $3y + 4x = 20$
5) $y + 4x = -6$, $3x + 7y = 8$
6) $12x + y = -1$, $4x - 2y = 16$
7) $x = 2y - 1$, $3y - 2x + 6 = 0$
8) $x + 10y = 1$, $8y + 2x = 8$
9) $y = \frac{1}{4}x + 3$, $x + 8y = 18$
10) $x = y + 9$, $3x + y = 7$

A SIMULTANEOUS EQUATIONS (2)

Elimination

This is done by making sure first that both equations have a matching letter-term (e.g. x, y, 2x, 3y, 5x, etc). Depending on the signs of the matching terms, the equations are either added or subtracted to eliminate (get rid of) one of the letters.

e.g. Solve the simultaneous equations

$3x + 2y = 19$ ....equation ①

$x - 2y = 1$ ....equation ②

Both equations have a 2y term. The signs are unlike (+ –).
If equations ① and ② are added, the y terms are eliminated

$3x + 2y = 19$ ... ①

$x - 2y = 1$ ... ②

$4x = 20$ so $x = 5$

Now substitute in either equation (whichever is simpler),
e.g. substitute in equation ①

$15 + 2y = 19$ so $y = 2$ $\begin{cases} x = 5 \\ y = 2 \end{cases}$

---

e.g. (2) Solve $3x + 4y = 15$ .... ①

$3x - 3y = -6$ .... ②

Both equations have a 3x term. The signs are like (+ +).
If ② is subtracted from ①, the x terms are eliminated

$7y = 21$, so $y = 3$

Substituting in either equation, $x = 1$ $\begin{cases} x = 1 \\ y = 3 \end{cases}$

---

e.g. (3) Solve $4x - 2y = 10$ .... ①

$3x + y = 15$ .... ②

No terms are similar, so MULTIPLY all through one (or both) of the equations to give similar terms

Multiply ② by 2 $6x + 2y = 30$ .... ③

$4x - 2y = 10$ .... ①

Signs are unlike, so add ③ and ①

$10x = 40$, so $x = 4$

Substituting in either equation, $y = 3$ $\begin{cases} x = 4 \\ y = 3 \end{cases}$

If terms are arranged unsuitably in the question, rearrange them so that x is beneath x, y is beneath y, etc. Be careful to change signs of terms where necessary.

a

Solve by adding the equations

1) $a + b = 12$
   $a - b = 2$

2) $3r - t = 1$
   $2r + t = 9$

3) $2x + y = 18$
   $4x - y = 24$

4) $2k + m = 7$
   $4k - m = 8$

5) $d + 2h = 22$
   $3d - 2h = 26$

6) $a + b = 3$
   $a - b = 5$

7) $2x - y = -10$
   $x + y = 1$

8) $3m + 2n = 25$
   $4m - 2n = 10$

9) $4j - k = 12$
   $3j + k = 9$

10) $2p + 6q = 0$
    $p - 6q = 18$

---

b

Solve by subtracting one equation from the other

1) $5x + y = 22$
   $3x + y = 14$

2) $6p - q = 13$
   $2p - q = 1$

3) $j + 7k = 53$
   $j + 4k = 35$

4) $3e + d = 8$
   $2e + d = 8$

5) $3v + t = 26$
   $3v - 4t = 1$

6) $4x - 2y = 6$
   $x - 2y = 0$

7) $3b + a = 7$
   $b + a = 1$

8) $4h + 7m = 4$
   $4h - 4m = 48$

9) $3s - 5w = 0$
   $s - 5w = -10$

10) $2n - p = 7$
    $2n + 2p = 4$

---

c

Solve these simultaneous equations

1) $2x + y = 7$
   $4x - y = 5$

2) $2x + 3y = 15$
   $2x + y = 7$

3) $x + 3y = 23$
   $2x - y = 4$

4) $3x + 5y = 4$
   $x + y = 0$

5) $x + 2y = 8$
   $3x - 3y = 15$

6) $4x - 3y = 2$
   $x + 2y = -5$

7) $2x - 3y = -1$
   $3x - 2y = 6$

8) $4x + y = 7$
   $x + 2y = 14$

9) $2x + 5y = 0$
   $4x - y = 11$

10) $5x + y = 13$
    $2x - y = 8$

11) $2x + y = 20$
    $x + 4y = 10$

12) $3x - 8y = 2$
    $2x + 4y = 6$

13) $2x + 3y = 11$
    $5x + 2y = 11$

14) $2x + 3y = -7$
    $4x - 2y = 10$

15) $x - 3y = 0$
    $y - 3x = 16$

16) $3x + 2y = 123$
    $4x = 3y + 28$

17) $3x - 4y = 6$
    $y - 5x = 7$

18) $x - 6y = 4$
    $3x - 7y = 1$

19) $4y - 2x = 12$
    $3x - 2y = 2$

20) $y - 2x = 9$
    $2y + 8x = 12$

SIMULTANEOUS EQUATIONS(3)

Graphical method (By drawing graphs)

Simultaneous equations can sometimes be solved quite easily by drawing the graph of each equation on squared or graph paper. The intersection of the graphs is the solution of the equations.

e.g. Solve these simultaneous equations by drawing graphs

$y = x + 3$

$y = 6 - 2x$

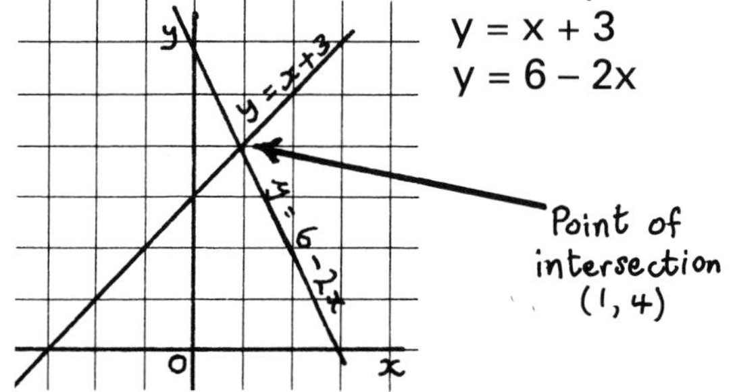

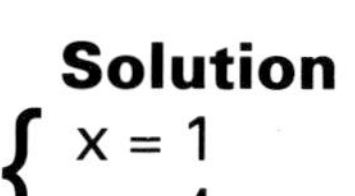

Solution

$\begin{cases} x = 1 \\ y = 4 \end{cases}$

Problems

e.g. (1)

JACK'S CAFÉ
2 beefburgers
3 eggs
TOTAL 33p

JACK'S CAFÉ
3 beefburgers
1 egg
TOTAL 32p

How much does each beefburger cost?
How much does each egg cost?

$$2b + 3e = 33$$
$$3b + e = 32$$

By either substitution (page 6) or elimination (page 8),

$\begin{cases} b = 9 \\ e = 5 \end{cases}$ Each beefburger costs 9p
Each egg costs 5p

---

e.g. (2) Aunt Peg has in her purse x 50p coins, y 20p coins and no other coins. Altogether she has 13 coins and their total is £4.10.

(a) How many 50p coins are there?
(b) How many 20p coins are there?

Equation for number of coins $x + y = 13$
Equation for amount of money $50x + 20y = 410$
By substitution or elimination

$\begin{cases} x = 5 \\ y = 8 \end{cases}$ There are 5 50p coins
There are 8 20p coins

a Solve these simultaneous equations by drawing graphs. Use squared paper or graph paper

1) $y = x + 2$
   $y = 5 - 2x$
2) $y = 3x - 2$
   $x + y = -6$
3) $y = \frac{1}{2}x - 1$
   $y = x - 4$
4) $y = 4x + 1$
   $y = 2x + 2$
5) $x + y = 1$
   $y = 2x + 4$
6) $y = 4 - 3x$
   $y = 2x - 1$
7) $y = x$
   $y = 4x + 6$
8) $y = x + 1$
   $2x + y = 4$
9) $y = 2x + 3$
   $y + x = -6$
10) $y = 8 - x$
   $y = x - 2$

Write these problems as simultaneous equations and find the answers.

1) 12 toffees and 4 mints cost 44p; 7 toffees and 5 mints cost 31p. How much does each toffee cost?

2) Jamie spent 86p on 2 cans of orange drink and 3 packets of crisps; Carla spent 80p on 3 cans of orange and 1 packet of crisps. Find the cost of (i) a can of orange, (ii) a packet of crisps.

3) The sum of Christine's and Fiona's ages is 23 and the difference between their ages is 5. Christine is the older girl. How old is she?

4) Two footballs and six tennis balls cost £16; three footballs and five tennis balls cost £22. Find how much a football costs.

5) 3 similar buckets and 5 similar jugs hold 32 litres altogether; 2 buckets and 12 jugs hold 30 litres altogether. How many litres does each bucket hold?

6) The sum of two whole numbers x and y is 63. The difference between the same two numbers is 35. What are the two numbers?

7) The Smith family (2 adults and 3 children) went by train to the seaside. Their tickets cost £24 altogether. The Green family (3 adults and 4 children) went on the same journey and it cost them £34. How much was (i) an adult ticket? (ii) a child's ticket?

8) John has x 10p coins and y 5p coins. Altogether he has 31 coins and their total value is £2.40. Find how many 10p coins he has.

9) Four large boxes and three small boxes piled one on top of another reach a height of 168cm. Three large boxes and four small boxes reach a height of 154cm. How high is a small box?

10) Mohinder buys 2 fritters and a bag of chips for £1.25. Dalip buys 3 fritters and 2 bags of chips for £2.05. Ranjid buys 1 fritter and 3 bags of chips. How much does he pay?

A MATRICES (1)

A MATRIX is an arrangement of numbers in rows and/or columns within brackets. If there are more than one, they are called MATRICES (pronounced may-tree-seez).

Addition

Each matrix in addition and subtraction must have the same pattern of numbers. Add the number in the first matrix to the number in the same position in the other matrix (or matrices).

e.g. (1) $\begin{pmatrix} 2 & 3 \end{pmatrix} + \begin{pmatrix} 5 & 1 \end{pmatrix} = \begin{pmatrix} 2+5 & 3+1 \end{pmatrix} = \begin{pmatrix} 7 & 4 \end{pmatrix}$

e.g. (2) $\begin{pmatrix} 4 \\ 2 \end{pmatrix} + \begin{pmatrix} 6 \\ 5 \end{pmatrix} + \begin{pmatrix} 1 \\ 6 \end{pmatrix} = \begin{pmatrix} 4+6+1 \\ 2+5+6 \end{pmatrix} = \begin{pmatrix} 11 \\ 13 \end{pmatrix}$

e.g. (3) $\begin{pmatrix} 5 & 1 \\ 0 & 6 \end{pmatrix} + \begin{pmatrix} 2 & 7 \\ 3 & 3 \end{pmatrix} = \begin{pmatrix} 5+2 & 1+7 \\ 0+3 & 6+3 \end{pmatrix} = \begin{pmatrix} 7 & 8 \\ 3 & 9 \end{pmatrix}$

Be careful with negative numbers

e.g. (4) $\begin{pmatrix} 8 & -1 \\ 2 & 3 \end{pmatrix} + \begin{pmatrix} 0 & 6 \\ -5 & 2 \end{pmatrix} = \begin{pmatrix} 8+0 & -1+6 \\ 2+-5 & 3+2 \end{pmatrix} = \begin{pmatrix} 8 & 5 \\ -3 & 5 \end{pmatrix}$

B **Subtraction** Subtract the number in the second matrix from the number in the same position in the first matrix

e.g. (1) $\begin{pmatrix} 12 & 7 \end{pmatrix} - \begin{pmatrix} 4 & 5 \end{pmatrix} = \begin{pmatrix} 12-4 & 7-5 \end{pmatrix} = \begin{pmatrix} 8 & 2 \end{pmatrix}$

e.g. (2) $\begin{pmatrix} 5 \\ 2 \\ 9 \end{pmatrix} - \begin{pmatrix} 1 \\ 5 \\ 2 \end{pmatrix} = \begin{pmatrix} 5-1 \\ 2-5 \\ 9-2 \end{pmatrix} = \begin{pmatrix} 4 \\ -3 \\ 7 \end{pmatrix}$

e.g. (3) $\begin{pmatrix} 4 & -2 & 8 \\ -3 & 3 & 0 \end{pmatrix} - \begin{pmatrix} 1 & 7 & 6 \\ -2 & -8 & 5 \end{pmatrix} = \begin{pmatrix} 3 & -9 & 2 \\ -1 & 11 & -5 \end{pmatrix}$

C **Multiplication by a number**

Multiply all the numbers in the matrix by the number outside, e.g. (1) $\begin{pmatrix} 4 & 3 \\ 0 & 6 \end{pmatrix} \times 3 = \begin{pmatrix} 12 & 9 \\ 0 & 18 \end{pmatrix}$

e.g. (2) $5\begin{pmatrix} 2 & -1 \\ 3 & 0 \end{pmatrix} = \begin{pmatrix} 10 & -5 \\ 15 & 0 \end{pmatrix}$

e.g. (3) $\frac{1}{2}\begin{pmatrix} 12 & -8 \\ 7 & 26 \end{pmatrix} = \begin{pmatrix} 6 & -4 \\ 3\frac{1}{2} & 13 \end{pmatrix}$

D **Matrix patterns** A matrix with one row and two columns is a 1 x 2 matrix, e.g. $\begin{pmatrix} 3 & 4 \end{pmatrix}$; with two rows and three columns it is a 2 x 3 matrix, e.g.

$\begin{pmatrix} 1 & 5 & 1 \\ 2 & -4 & 0 \end{pmatrix}$, etc.

a

Try these additions

1) $(1 \quad 4) + (5 \quad 3)$

2) $\begin{pmatrix} 6 \\ 3 \end{pmatrix} + \begin{pmatrix} 2 \\ 7 \end{pmatrix}$

3) $(0 \quad 3) + (2 \quad 7)$

4) $\begin{pmatrix} 1 \\ 2 \\ 4 \end{pmatrix} + \begin{pmatrix} 6 \\ 3 \\ 11 \end{pmatrix}$

5) $\begin{pmatrix} -10 \\ 4 \end{pmatrix} + \begin{pmatrix} -2 \\ -4 \end{pmatrix}$

6) $\begin{pmatrix} 8 & 2 \\ 12 & 3 \end{pmatrix} + \begin{pmatrix} 5 & 11 \\ 1 & 10 \end{pmatrix}$

7) $\begin{pmatrix} 2 & 0 \\ 5 & -7 \end{pmatrix} + \begin{pmatrix} 4 & 1 \\ -3 & 3 \end{pmatrix}$

8) $(5 \quad 9 \quad -4) + (-5 \quad 9 \quad -4)$

9) $\begin{pmatrix} 4 & -7 \\ -3 & 4 \end{pmatrix} + \begin{pmatrix} 0 & 3 \\ 5 & -8 \end{pmatrix} + \begin{pmatrix} 1 & 2 \\ 2 & 1 \end{pmatrix}$

10) $\begin{pmatrix} 0 & 5 \\ 3 & -6 \\ 10 & 2 \end{pmatrix} + \begin{pmatrix} 7 & -4 \\ 1 & -2 \\ -1 & 6 \end{pmatrix}$

---

b

Try these subtractions. Remember that – – has the same effect as +

1) $\begin{pmatrix} 5 \\ 7 \end{pmatrix} - \begin{pmatrix} 2 \\ 1 \end{pmatrix}$

2) $(6 \quad 9) - (6 \quad 5)$

3) $\begin{pmatrix} 1 & 4 \\ 3 & 7 \end{pmatrix} - \begin{pmatrix} 0 & 2 \\ 1 & 4 \end{pmatrix}$

4) $(6 \quad 2 \quad 3) - (2 \quad 5 \quad 0)$

5) $\begin{pmatrix} 5 \\ 6 \\ 1 \end{pmatrix} - \begin{pmatrix} 8 \\ 4 \\ 1 \end{pmatrix}$

6) $(4 \quad 3) - (-2 \quad 5)$

7) $\begin{pmatrix} 5 & 2 & -2 \\ 0 & 4 & 7 \end{pmatrix} - \begin{pmatrix} 1 & -2 & 2 \\ 4 & -1 & 6 \end{pmatrix}$

8) $\begin{pmatrix} -1 & -2 \\ -3 & -6 \end{pmatrix} - \begin{pmatrix} 2 & 4 \\ -4 & -6 \end{pmatrix}$

9) $(3 \quad 1 \quad -5) - (4 \quad -1 \quad 3)$

10) $\begin{pmatrix} 0 & 7 \\ 3 & 11 \\ 2 & 4 \end{pmatrix} - \begin{pmatrix} 7 & -1 \\ 0 & -8 \\ 1 & -3 \end{pmatrix}$

---

c

1) $\begin{pmatrix} 3 & 2 \\ 5 & 1 \end{pmatrix} \times 4$

2) $(5 \quad 7 \quad 2) \times 2$

3) $3\begin{pmatrix} 1 & 3 \\ 0 & -1 \end{pmatrix}$

4) $\begin{pmatrix} 1 & -1 \\ 2 & 2 \\ 3 & 0 \end{pmatrix} \times 5$

5) $6\begin{pmatrix} 3 & 2 & -1 \\ -1 & 1 & 0 \end{pmatrix}$

6) $\frac{1}{3}\begin{pmatrix} 6 & 3 & 15 \\ -12 & 0 & 9 \end{pmatrix}$

7) $4\begin{pmatrix} \frac{1}{2} & \frac{1}{4} \\ -1 & 1\frac{1}{2} \end{pmatrix}$

8) $-2\begin{pmatrix} 6 & 5 \\ 4 & -2 \\ -3 & 1 \end{pmatrix}$

9) $x\begin{pmatrix} 2 & x \\ y & 0 \end{pmatrix}$

10) $-\frac{1}{2}\begin{pmatrix} 8 & -2 & 14 \\ 4 & 0 & 16 \end{pmatrix}$

A MATRICES (2) - MULTIPLICATION

Compatible and incompatible matrices

Matrices may be multiplied only if they are COMPATIBLE for multiplication. The second matrix is PRE-MULTIPLIED by the first. **Each ROW in the first matrix must have the same pattern as each COLUMN in the second matrix,** e.g.

$$\begin{pmatrix}4 & 3 & 1\end{pmatrix}\begin{pmatrix}0\\5\\7\end{pmatrix}$$

3 numbers in row — 3 numbers in column

$$\begin{pmatrix}6 & 5\end{pmatrix}\begin{pmatrix}3 & 0 & 2\\4 & 1 & -2\end{pmatrix}$$

2 numbers in row — 2 numbers in column

If the matrices are INCOMPATIBLE (pattern of rows in the first does not match pattern of columns in the second) they cannot be multiplied, e.g.

$$\begin{pmatrix}3 & 2\end{pmatrix}\begin{pmatrix}5\\1\\0\end{pmatrix}$$

2 numbers in row — 3 numbers in column

$$\begin{pmatrix}4\\7\end{pmatrix}\begin{pmatrix}5 & 1\\6 & 2\end{pmatrix}$$

1 number in row — 2 numbers in column

B Multiplication

e.g. $\begin{pmatrix}2 & 5\end{pmatrix}\begin{pmatrix}4\\3\end{pmatrix}$

*The ROW in the first matrix multiplies the COLUMN in the second matrix, so that the **left-hand number** of the first matrix multiplies the **top number** of the second matrix (2 x 4 = 8). Then the next number multiplies the next number (5 x 3 = 15), and so on.

*These results are added together to give the answer 8 + 15 = 23

$$\begin{pmatrix}2 & 5\end{pmatrix}\begin{pmatrix}4\\3\end{pmatrix} = \begin{pmatrix}23\end{pmatrix}$$

---

e.g. $\begin{pmatrix}1 & 6\end{pmatrix}\begin{pmatrix}2\\-1\end{pmatrix}$

Left x Top = 1 x 2 = 2

Right x Bottom = 6x −1 = −6

2 + −6 = −4

$$\begin{pmatrix}1 & 6\end{pmatrix}\begin{pmatrix}2\\-1\end{pmatrix} = \begin{pmatrix}-4\end{pmatrix}$$

e.g. $\begin{pmatrix}3 & 0 & 4\end{pmatrix}\begin{pmatrix}7\\8\\4\end{pmatrix}$

Left x Top = 3 x 7 = 21

Middle x Middle = 0 x 8 = 0

Right x Bottom = 4 x 4 = 16

21 + 0 + 16 = 37

$$\begin{pmatrix}3 & 0 & 4\end{pmatrix}\begin{pmatrix}7\\8\\4\end{pmatrix} = \begin{pmatrix}37\end{pmatrix}$$

a

Copy each pair of matrices and write whether it is COMPATIBLE (can be multiplied) or INCOMPATIBLE (cannot be multiplied)

1) $\begin{pmatrix}5 & 3 & 7\end{pmatrix}\begin{pmatrix}1\\2\\0\end{pmatrix}$

2) $\begin{pmatrix}2 & 4\end{pmatrix}\begin{pmatrix}6 & 1 & 5 & 0\\3 & 4 & 3 & 2\end{pmatrix}$

3) $\begin{pmatrix}6 & 0 & 1\end{pmatrix}\begin{pmatrix}1 & 2 & 5\\3 & 2 & -2\end{pmatrix}$

4) $\begin{pmatrix}6 & -1 & -2\end{pmatrix}\begin{pmatrix}5 & 1\\2 & 4\\3 & 0\end{pmatrix}$

5) $\begin{pmatrix}8 & 7\end{pmatrix}\begin{pmatrix}4 & 0\\4 & 1\\-2 & 3\end{pmatrix}$

b

Multiply these matrices

1) $\begin{pmatrix}4 & 3\end{pmatrix}\begin{pmatrix}1\\2\end{pmatrix}$

2) $\begin{pmatrix}5 & 0\end{pmatrix}\begin{pmatrix}3\\2\end{pmatrix}$

3) $\begin{pmatrix}6 & -1\end{pmatrix}\begin{pmatrix}2\\5\end{pmatrix}$

4) $\begin{pmatrix}5 & 2 & 3\end{pmatrix}\begin{pmatrix}1\\4\\7\end{pmatrix}$

5) $\begin{pmatrix}0 & 3\end{pmatrix}\begin{pmatrix}5\\0\end{pmatrix}$

6) $\begin{pmatrix}4 & 1 & 2 & 2\end{pmatrix}\begin{pmatrix}0\\3\\2\\-1\end{pmatrix}$

7) $\begin{pmatrix}-2 & -1\end{pmatrix}\begin{pmatrix}4\\-6\end{pmatrix}$

8) $\begin{pmatrix}1 & 0 & 1\end{pmatrix}\begin{pmatrix}12\\3\\-6\end{pmatrix}$

9) $\begin{pmatrix}11 & 7 & 12\end{pmatrix}\begin{pmatrix}6\\0\\1\end{pmatrix}$

10) $\begin{pmatrix}1 & 2 & 3\end{pmatrix}\begin{pmatrix}3\\2\\1\end{pmatrix}$

c

Try these multiplications

1) $\begin{pmatrix}4 & 8 & 2\end{pmatrix}\begin{pmatrix}2\\1\\3\end{pmatrix}$

2) $\begin{pmatrix}5 & 5\end{pmatrix}\begin{pmatrix}4\\3\end{pmatrix}$

3) $\begin{pmatrix}-1 & 0 & 1 & 0\end{pmatrix}\begin{pmatrix}3\\-3\\-2\\1\end{pmatrix}$

4) $\begin{pmatrix}-4 & -6\end{pmatrix}\begin{pmatrix}-3\\-4\end{pmatrix}$

5) $\begin{pmatrix}3 & 19\end{pmatrix}\begin{pmatrix}17\\12\end{pmatrix}$

6) $\begin{pmatrix}0 & 5 & 2\end{pmatrix}\begin{pmatrix}4\\5\\10\end{pmatrix}$

7) $\begin{pmatrix}-2 & -3 & 2\end{pmatrix}\begin{pmatrix}7\\-6\\-2\end{pmatrix}$

8) $\begin{pmatrix}24 & -10\end{pmatrix}\begin{pmatrix}10\\-16\end{pmatrix}$

9) $\begin{pmatrix}\mathbf{x} & 3\end{pmatrix}\begin{pmatrix}4\\\mathbf{x}\end{pmatrix}$

10) $\begin{pmatrix}6 & \mathbf{n} & 2\end{pmatrix}\begin{pmatrix}\mathbf{n}\\5\\4\end{pmatrix}$

MATRICES (3) - MULTIPLICATION

Multiplication with several rows and columns

What will the answer look like?

e.g. A **1** x 2 matrix ⚀⚁ pre-multiplying a 2 x **3** matrix ⚂⚂ will give a **1** x **3** matrix as the answer

⚀⚁⚂⚂ e.g. $(3\ \ 4)\begin{pmatrix}4 & 1 & 0\\3 & 2 & 5\end{pmatrix} = (24\ \ 11\ \ 20)$

e.g. (2) A **2** x 3 matrix pre-multiplying a 3 x **1** matrix will give a **2** x **1** matrix as the answer

⚂⚂⚂⚀ e.g. $\begin{pmatrix}1 & 2 & 0\\4 & -1 & 3\end{pmatrix}\begin{pmatrix}1\\3\\6\end{pmatrix} = \begin{pmatrix}7\\19\end{pmatrix}$ etc.

B

Multiplication with more than one column

e.g. (1) $(3\ \ 2)\begin{pmatrix}5 & 4 & 0\\1 & 6 & 4\end{pmatrix}$

$(3\ \ 2)\begin{pmatrix}5\\1\end{pmatrix} = 15 + 2 = (17\qquad)$

$(3\ \ 2)\begin{pmatrix}4\\6\end{pmatrix} = 12 + 12 = (\quad 24\quad)$

$(3\ \ 2)\begin{pmatrix}0\\4\end{pmatrix} = 0 + 8 = (\qquad 8)$

Answer $(17\ \ 24\ \ 8)$

e.g. (2) $(6\ \ 3\ \ 2)\begin{pmatrix}5 & -1\\1 & 0\\2 & 4\end{pmatrix}$

$(6\ \ 3\ \ 2)\begin{pmatrix}5\\1\\2\end{pmatrix} = 30 + 3 + 4 = (37\quad)$

$(6\ \ 3\ \ 2)\begin{pmatrix}-1\\0\\4\end{pmatrix} = -6 + 0 + 8 = (\quad 2)$

Answer $(37\ \ 2)$

Multiplication with more than one row

e.g. $\begin{pmatrix}1 & 2\\5 & 1\end{pmatrix}\begin{pmatrix}3\\1\end{pmatrix}$

Top row $(1\ \ 2)\begin{pmatrix}3\\1\end{pmatrix} = 3 + 2 = (5)$

Bottom row $(5\ \ 1)\begin{pmatrix}3\\1\end{pmatrix} = 15 + 1 = (16)$

Answer $\begin{pmatrix}5\\16\end{pmatrix}$

---

e.g. (2) $\begin{pmatrix}2 & 4\\1 & 3\end{pmatrix}\begin{pmatrix}-1 & 2\\5 & 0\end{pmatrix}$

Top row $(2\ \ 4)\begin{pmatrix}-1\\5\end{pmatrix} = -2 + 20 = (18\qquad)$

$(2\ \ 4)\begin{pmatrix}2\\0\end{pmatrix} = 4 + 0 = (18\ \ \ 4)$

Bottom row $(1\ \ 3)\begin{pmatrix}-1\\5\end{pmatrix} = -1 + 15 = \begin{pmatrix}18 & 4\\14 & \end{pmatrix}$

$(1\ \ 3)\begin{pmatrix}2\\0\end{pmatrix} = 2 + 0 = \begin{pmatrix}18 & 4\\14 & 2\end{pmatrix}$

a

Write down the pattern of matrix (e.g. 3 x 2) which will result from these multiplications

1) 1 x 3 premultiplying 3 x 1
2) 2 x 1 premultiplying 1 x 3
3) 3 x 2 premultiplying 2 x 2
4) 1 x 2 premultiplying 2 x 3
5) 2 x 3 premultiplying 3 x 2
6) 1 x 2 premultiplying 2 x 2
7) 4 x 1 premultiplying 1 x 3
8) 3 x 3 premultiplying 3 x 2
9) 2 x 4 premultiplying 4 x 5
10) 3 x 1 premultiplying 1 x 4

b

Multiply these matrices

1) $\begin{pmatrix} 1 & 2 \end{pmatrix}\begin{pmatrix} 3 & 4 \\ 1 & 0 \end{pmatrix}$

2) $\begin{pmatrix} 3 & 5 \end{pmatrix}\begin{pmatrix} 2 & 1 \\ 1 & 6 \end{pmatrix}$

3) $\begin{pmatrix} 2 & 4 \end{pmatrix}\begin{pmatrix} 1 & 2 & 0 \\ 0 & 3 & 5 \end{pmatrix}$

4) $\begin{pmatrix} 2 & 3 & 1 \end{pmatrix}\begin{pmatrix} 4 & 3 \\ 1 & 0 \\ 2 & 1 \end{pmatrix}$

5) $\begin{pmatrix} -1 & -2 \end{pmatrix}\begin{pmatrix} 3 & 1 \\ 7 & 2 \end{pmatrix}$

6) $\begin{pmatrix} 0 & -1 \end{pmatrix}\begin{pmatrix} 6 & 5 \\ 3 & 2 \end{pmatrix}$

7) $\begin{pmatrix} 6 & -3 \end{pmatrix}\begin{pmatrix} 0 & 3 & -2 \\ 1 & 2 & 2 \end{pmatrix}$

8) $\begin{pmatrix} 2 & 0 & 5 \end{pmatrix}\begin{pmatrix} -2 & 2 & -3 \\ 9 & 4 & -1 \\ 3 & 1 & 2 \end{pmatrix}$

9) $\begin{pmatrix} 8 & -1 \end{pmatrix}\begin{pmatrix} 1 & 0 \\ 2 & -3 \end{pmatrix}$

10) $\begin{pmatrix} -3 & 1 & -2 \end{pmatrix}\begin{pmatrix} -2 \\ 4 \\ -5 \end{pmatrix}$

11) $\begin{pmatrix} 2 & 1 & 3 & 4 \end{pmatrix}\begin{pmatrix} 1 & 1 \\ 2 & -4 \\ 0 & 3 \\ 2 & 2 \end{pmatrix}$

12) $\begin{pmatrix} 15 & 22 \end{pmatrix}\begin{pmatrix} 1 \\ -7 \end{pmatrix}$

13) $\begin{pmatrix} 2 & -1 & 3 & 4 \end{pmatrix}\begin{pmatrix} 4 \\ 1 \\ 2 \\ -3 \end{pmatrix}$

14) $\begin{pmatrix} -1 & 1 \end{pmatrix}\begin{pmatrix} 4 & 1 & 5 & 0 \\ 0 & 3 & 2 & 1 \end{pmatrix}$

15) $\begin{pmatrix} 3 & 2 & -1 \end{pmatrix}\begin{pmatrix} 1 & 3 & 0 \\ 2 & -1 & 5 \\ 4 & 3 & 1 \end{pmatrix}$

c

Multiply these matrices

1) $\begin{pmatrix} 2 & 1 \\ 1 & 3 \end{pmatrix}\begin{pmatrix} 5 & 1 \\ 2 & 6 \end{pmatrix}$

2) $\begin{pmatrix} 4 & 0 \\ 0 & 3 \end{pmatrix}\begin{pmatrix} 1 & 2 \\ 4 & 3 \end{pmatrix}$

3) $\begin{pmatrix} 2 \\ 3 \end{pmatrix}\begin{pmatrix} 6 & 4 \end{pmatrix}$

4) $\begin{pmatrix} 1 & 0 \\ 0 & 1 \end{pmatrix}\begin{pmatrix} 3 & 4 \\ 6 & 2 \end{pmatrix}$

5) $\begin{pmatrix} 2 & 6 \\ 3 & 7 \end{pmatrix}\begin{pmatrix} 5 \\ 4 \end{pmatrix}$

6) $\begin{pmatrix} 1 & 3 \\ 3 & 1 \end{pmatrix}\begin{pmatrix} 4 & 3 & 0 \\ 1 & 6 & 5 \end{pmatrix}$

7) $\begin{pmatrix} 8 \\ 2 \end{pmatrix}\begin{pmatrix} 3 & 5 \end{pmatrix}$

8) $\begin{pmatrix} -1 & 0 \\ 2 & -1 \end{pmatrix}\begin{pmatrix} 3 & 4 \\ 6 & 2 \end{pmatrix}$

9) $\begin{pmatrix} 4 & 1 \\ 0 & 2 \\ 1 & 5 \end{pmatrix}\begin{pmatrix} 2 & 1 \\ 1 & 2 \end{pmatrix}$

10) $\begin{pmatrix} 2 & 4 & 1 \\ 1 & 2 & 3 \end{pmatrix}\begin{pmatrix} 6 \\ 1 \\ 2 \end{pmatrix}$

11) $\begin{pmatrix} 1 \\ 4 \\ 3 \end{pmatrix}\begin{pmatrix} 6 & 7 \end{pmatrix}$

12) $\begin{pmatrix} -3 & 9 \\ 0 & -2 \end{pmatrix}\begin{pmatrix} -2 & 0 \\ 5 & -1 \end{pmatrix}$

13) $\begin{pmatrix} -1 & -2 \\ -4 & -1 \end{pmatrix}\begin{pmatrix} 0 & -1 & 1 \\ 1 & 0 & 0 \end{pmatrix}$

14) $\begin{pmatrix} 13 & 11 \\ 11 & 13 \end{pmatrix}\begin{pmatrix} 13 \\ 11 \end{pmatrix}$

15) $\begin{pmatrix} 3 & -1 \\ 0 & 2 \\ -1 & -2 \\ 2 & 4 \end{pmatrix}\begin{pmatrix} -2 & 3 & 0 \\ 1 & -4 & 1 \end{pmatrix}$

MATRICES (4)

Determinant of a matrix

In the matrix $\begin{pmatrix} A & B \\ C & D \end{pmatrix}$ the determinant is (A x D) – (C x B)

e.g. the determinant of $\begin{pmatrix} 4 & 1 \\ 3 & 2 \end{pmatrix}$ is (4 x 2) – (3 x 1) = 5

e.g. the determinant of $\begin{pmatrix} 7 & -5 \\ -4 & 3 \end{pmatrix}$ is (7 x 3) – (–4 x –5) = 1

Inverse matrix of $\begin{pmatrix} A & B \\ C & D \end{pmatrix}$ is found by (i) changing the positions of A and D, (ii) making C and B negative, (iii) multiplying by the reciprocal of the determinant $\frac{1}{\text{determinant}}$

e.g. the inverse matrix of $\begin{pmatrix} 4 & 5 \\ 2 & 3 \end{pmatrix}$ which has determinant 2, is

$$\frac{1}{2}\begin{pmatrix} 3 & -5 \\ -2 & 4 \end{pmatrix} \quad \text{or} \quad \begin{pmatrix} 1\frac{1}{2} & -2\frac{1}{2} \\ -1 & 2 \end{pmatrix}$$

e.g. the inverse matrix of $\begin{pmatrix} 1 & -3 \\ -2 & 9 \end{pmatrix}$ which has determinant 3, is

$$\frac{1}{3}\begin{pmatrix} 9 & 3 \\ 2 & 1 \end{pmatrix} \quad \text{or} \quad \begin{pmatrix} 3 & 1 \\ \frac{2}{3} & \frac{1}{3} \end{pmatrix}$$

Coded messages by matrices

Messages can be sent in code by using matrices. This form of coding is almost impossible to decode except by the person using the decoding matrix, e.g.

using A = 1, B = 2, C = 3, etc., the message PICKLE would be 16 9 3 11 12 5 which could be arranged into a 2 x 3 matrix $\begin{pmatrix} 16 & 9 & 3 \\ 11 & 12 & 5 \end{pmatrix}$

The sender of the message uses a coding matrix **with determinant 1**, e.g. $\begin{pmatrix} 2 & 1 \\ 5 & 3 \end{pmatrix}$ and the receiver uses its INVERSE MATRIX $\begin{pmatrix} 3 & -1 \\ -5 & 2 \end{pmatrix}$

The sender premultiplies by the coding matrix

$$\begin{pmatrix} 2 & 1 \\ 5 & 3 \end{pmatrix} \begin{pmatrix} 16 & 9 & 3 \\ 11 & 12 & 5 \end{pmatrix} = \begin{pmatrix} 43 & 30 & 11 \\ 113 & 81 & 30 \end{pmatrix}$$

CODING MATRIX *MESSAGE* *MESSAGE IN CODE*

The receiver then premultiplies by the inverse (decoding) matrix

$$\begin{pmatrix} 3 & -1 \\ -5 & 2 \end{pmatrix} \begin{pmatrix} 43 & 30 & 11 \\ 113 & 81 & 30 \end{pmatrix} = \begin{pmatrix} 16 & 9 & 3 \\ 11 & 12 & 5 \end{pmatrix}$$

DECODING MATRIX *MESSAGE IN CODE* *MESSAGE*

a

Find the determinant of each of these matrices

1) $\begin{pmatrix} 4 & 1 \\ 7 & 2 \end{pmatrix}$ 2) $\begin{pmatrix} 9 & 5 \\ 3 & 2 \end{pmatrix}$ 3) $\begin{pmatrix} 3 & 1 \\ 1 & 3 \end{pmatrix}$ 4) $\begin{pmatrix} 13 & 9 \\ 7 & 5 \end{pmatrix}$

5) $\begin{pmatrix} 2 & 1\frac{1}{2} \\ 1 & 1 \end{pmatrix}$ 6) $\begin{pmatrix} 3 & 3 \\ 2 & 1 \end{pmatrix}$ 7) $\begin{pmatrix} 3 & -4 \\ -2 & 3 \end{pmatrix}$ 8) $\begin{pmatrix} 8 & 6 \\ 4 & 3 \end{pmatrix}$

9) $\begin{pmatrix} 6 & 3 \\ 3\frac{1}{2} & 2 \end{pmatrix}$ 10) $\begin{pmatrix} 2 & 4 \\ -1 & 3 \end{pmatrix}$

b

Find the inverse of each of these matrices. First find the determinant (d) of each matrix. Leave your answer in the form $\frac{1}{d}\begin{pmatrix} A & B \\ C & D \end{pmatrix}$

1) $\begin{pmatrix} 2 & 1 \\ 4 & 3 \end{pmatrix}$ 2) $\begin{pmatrix} 5 & 6 \\ 6 & 4 \end{pmatrix}$ 3) $\begin{pmatrix} 2 & 1 \\ -3 & 2 \end{pmatrix}$ 4) $\begin{pmatrix} 9 & -3 \\ -5 & 2 \end{pmatrix}$

5) $\begin{pmatrix} 4 & 0 \\ 1 & 1 \end{pmatrix}$ 6) $\begin{pmatrix} 2 & 3 \\ 1 & 2 \end{pmatrix}$ 7) $\begin{pmatrix} 4 & -7 \\ -5 & 9 \end{pmatrix}$ 8) $\begin{pmatrix} -2 & -3 \\ 3 & 7 \end{pmatrix}$

9) $\begin{pmatrix} 1 & 5 \\ \frac{1}{2} & 2 \end{pmatrix}$ 10) $\begin{pmatrix} 4 & 5 \\ 5 & 7 \end{pmatrix}$

c

Anthony sends messages to James using A = 1, B = 2, C = 3, D = 4, etc., and the coding matrix $\begin{pmatrix} 5 & 2 \\ 2 & 1 \end{pmatrix}$

The messages are (1) GO AWAY (2) HELP (3) STOP IT (4) DUCK (5) WELL DONE, and Anthony arranges them

1) $\begin{pmatrix} G & O & A \\ W & A & Y \end{pmatrix}$ 2) $\begin{pmatrix} H & E \\ L & P \end{pmatrix}$ 3) $\begin{pmatrix} S & T & O \\ P & I & T \end{pmatrix}$ 4) $\begin{pmatrix} D & U \\ C & K \end{pmatrix}$ 5) $\begin{pmatrix} W & E & L & L \\ D & O & N & E \end{pmatrix}$

(a) Write each message in number matrix form (b) Using Anthony's coding matrix, write each message in code

---

James uses the inverse matrix $\begin{pmatrix} 1 & -2 \\ -2 & 5 \end{pmatrix}$ to decode Anthony's messages. He receives these messages in code.

Try to work out what the messages are

6) $\begin{pmatrix} 125 & 37 & 112 \\ 53 & 16 & 46 \end{pmatrix}$ 7) $\begin{pmatrix} 133 & 45 \\ 55 & 22 \end{pmatrix}$ 8) $\begin{pmatrix} 38 & 75 & 124 & 63 \\ 16 & 33 & 51 & 29 \end{pmatrix}$

9) $\begin{pmatrix} 25 & 93 & 93 \\ 11 & 39 & 40 \end{pmatrix}$ 10) $\begin{pmatrix} 99 & 85 & 7 & 136 & 33 \\ 40 & 37 & 3 & 58 & 14 \end{pmatrix}$

A MATRICES (5)

Solving equations using matrices

e.g. By multiplying matrices, find the value of y

$$(y \quad 5)\begin{pmatrix}1\\ y\end{pmatrix} = (18)$$

$$(1y + 5y) = (18)$$

$$(6y) = (18) \qquad y = 3$$

e.g. (2) $(k \quad 7)\begin{pmatrix}3\\ -2\end{pmatrix} = (10)$

$$(3k - 14) = (10) \qquad k = 8$$

Simultaneous equations in matrix form

e.g. Find the values of x and y if $\begin{pmatrix}4 & x\\ y & 3\end{pmatrix}\begin{pmatrix}2\\ 6\end{pmatrix} = \begin{pmatrix}32\\ 22\end{pmatrix}$

Top row x column gives $(4 \times 2) + (x \times 6) = 6x + 8$

Bottom row *x* column gives $(y \times 2) + (3 \times 6) = 2y + 18$

$$\begin{matrix}6x + 8 & = & 32\\ 2y + 18 & & 22\end{matrix}$$

From the top row $6x + 8 = 32$, so $x = 4$

From the bottom row $2y + 18 = 22$, so $y = 2$ $\quad \begin{cases}x = 4\\ y = 2\end{cases}$

Try checking the answer by substituting for x and y in the original matrix $\begin{pmatrix}4 & 4\\ 2 & 3\end{pmatrix}\begin{pmatrix}2\\ 6\end{pmatrix} = \begin{pmatrix}32\\ 22\end{pmatrix}$

Solving simultaneous equations by matrices

e.g. $2x + 7y = 13$

$x + 5y = 8$

*Write in matrix form $\begin{pmatrix}2 & 7\\ 1 & 5\end{pmatrix}\begin{pmatrix}x\\ y\end{pmatrix} = \begin{pmatrix}13\\ 8\end{pmatrix}$

*Multiply both sides of the equation by the inverse matrix

$$\frac{1}{3}\begin{pmatrix}5 & -7\\ -1 & 2\end{pmatrix}\begin{pmatrix}2 & 7\\ 1 & 5\end{pmatrix}\begin{pmatrix}x\\ y\end{pmatrix} = \frac{1}{3}\begin{pmatrix}5 & -7\\ -1 & 2\end{pmatrix}\begin{pmatrix}13\\ 8\end{pmatrix}$$

$$\begin{pmatrix}x\\ y\end{pmatrix} = \frac{1}{3}\begin{pmatrix}9\\ 3\end{pmatrix}$$

$$\begin{pmatrix}x\\ y\end{pmatrix} = \begin{pmatrix}3\\ 1\end{pmatrix} \qquad \begin{cases}x = 3\\ y = 1\end{cases}$$

NOTE. Any matrix multiplied by its inverse matrix gives the matrix form of the number 1, e.g. in the above example

$$\frac{1}{3}\begin{pmatrix}5 & -7\\ -1 & 2\end{pmatrix}\begin{pmatrix}2 & 7\\ 1 & 5\end{pmatrix}\begin{pmatrix}x\\ y\end{pmatrix} = \begin{pmatrix}1 & 0\\ 0 & 1\end{pmatrix}\begin{pmatrix}x\\ y\end{pmatrix} = \begin{pmatrix}x\\ y\end{pmatrix}$$, etc.

a

Solve these equations

1) $\begin{pmatrix} a & 3 \end{pmatrix}\begin{pmatrix} 4 \\ a \end{pmatrix} = \begin{pmatrix} 21 \end{pmatrix}$

2) $\begin{pmatrix} 5 & c \end{pmatrix}\begin{pmatrix} c \\ 4 \end{pmatrix} = \begin{pmatrix} 9 \end{pmatrix}$

3) $\begin{pmatrix} 2 & t & 3 \end{pmatrix}\begin{pmatrix} t \\ 6 \\ 1 \end{pmatrix} = \begin{pmatrix} 19 \end{pmatrix}$

4) $\begin{pmatrix} d & 4 \\ 1 & d \end{pmatrix}\begin{pmatrix} 2 \\ 0 \end{pmatrix} = \begin{pmatrix} 12 \\ 2 \end{pmatrix}$

5) $\begin{pmatrix} h & 2 \end{pmatrix}\begin{pmatrix} 6 \\ -3 \end{pmatrix} = \begin{pmatrix} 0 \end{pmatrix}$

6) $\begin{pmatrix} 7 & 2 \end{pmatrix}\begin{pmatrix} 5 \\ a \end{pmatrix} = \begin{pmatrix} 19 \end{pmatrix}$

7) $\begin{pmatrix} m & 1 \end{pmatrix}\begin{pmatrix} 1 \\ 1 \end{pmatrix} = \begin{pmatrix} 0 \end{pmatrix}$

8) $\begin{pmatrix} 2x & 3 \end{pmatrix}\begin{pmatrix} 1 \\ -4 \end{pmatrix} = \begin{pmatrix} 10 \end{pmatrix}$

9) $\begin{pmatrix} -2 & -5 \end{pmatrix}\begin{pmatrix} -4 \\ f \end{pmatrix} = \begin{pmatrix} 28 \end{pmatrix}$

10) $\begin{pmatrix} y & 3 \end{pmatrix}\begin{pmatrix} y \\ 2 \end{pmatrix} = \begin{pmatrix} 22 \end{pmatrix}$

b

Find the values of x and y in each of these

1) $\begin{pmatrix} x & 2 \\ 3 & y \end{pmatrix}\begin{pmatrix} 4 \\ 5 \end{pmatrix} = \begin{pmatrix} 18 \\ 17 \end{pmatrix}$

2) $\begin{pmatrix} x & 0 \\ 0 & y \end{pmatrix}\begin{pmatrix} 3 \\ 2 \end{pmatrix} = \begin{pmatrix} 9 \\ 10 \end{pmatrix}$

3) $\begin{pmatrix} x & -1 \\ 3 & y \end{pmatrix}\begin{pmatrix} 2 \\ 4 \end{pmatrix} = \begin{pmatrix} 8 \\ 10 \end{pmatrix}$

4) $\begin{pmatrix} x & 2 \\ 1 & y \end{pmatrix}\begin{pmatrix} 4 \\ 3 \end{pmatrix} = \begin{pmatrix} 26 \\ 25 \end{pmatrix}$

5) $\begin{pmatrix} -3 & x \\ y & -2 \end{pmatrix}\begin{pmatrix} 1 \\ 5 \end{pmatrix} = \begin{pmatrix} 17 \\ 1 \end{pmatrix}$

6) $\begin{pmatrix} x & 1 \end{pmatrix}\begin{pmatrix} 5 & 2 \\ 1 & y \end{pmatrix} = \begin{pmatrix} 41 & 21 \end{pmatrix}$

7) $\begin{pmatrix} 6 & x \\ y & 7 \end{pmatrix}\begin{pmatrix} 4 \\ -2 \end{pmatrix} = \begin{pmatrix} 10 \\ 10 \end{pmatrix}$

8) $\begin{pmatrix} 5 & 0 \\ 0 & 4 \end{pmatrix}\begin{pmatrix} x \\ y \end{pmatrix} = \begin{pmatrix} 20 \\ 12 \end{pmatrix}$

9) $\begin{pmatrix} 1 & y \\ x & 2 \end{pmatrix}\begin{pmatrix} 6 \\ 5 \end{pmatrix} = \begin{pmatrix} -4 \\ 4 \end{pmatrix}$

10) $\begin{pmatrix} x & y \\ y & x \end{pmatrix}\begin{pmatrix} 3 \\ 2 \end{pmatrix} = \begin{pmatrix} 14 \\ 16 \end{pmatrix}$

c

Write these simultaneous equations in matrix form and solve them

1) $3x + y = 9$
$x + 2y = 8$

2) $4x + y = 8$
$7x + 2y = 15$

3) $3x + 7y = 23$
$x + 3y = 9$

4) $5x - y = 3$
$-2x + y = 0$

5) $3x + y = 10$
$8x + 3y = 27$

6) $5x + 6y = 38$
$2x + 3y = 17$

7) $3x - y = 7$
$2x + y = 3$

8) $2x + 3y = 25$
$x + 2y = 15$

9) $x + 3y = 7$
$3x + 13y = 25$

10) $3x - y = 12$
$5x + 2y = 9$

A MATRICES (6)

Information store

Matrices are sometimes used as a short, compact way of storing, or showing, information,

e.g. Garside School has four soccer teams: 1st, 2nd, 3rd and Junior. Their results last season (win, lose or draw) can be shown as a matrix

$$\begin{array}{c} \\ W \\ L \\ D \end{array} \begin{array}{c} \begin{array}{cccc} 1st & 2nd & 3rd & Jun \end{array} \\ \begin{pmatrix} 9 & 3 & 4 & 6 \\ 5 & 4 & 4 & 0 \\ 2 & 3 & 1 & 3 \end{pmatrix} \end{array}$$

This matrix shows that the 1st team won 9 times, lost 5 times and drew twice, etc.

In the local schools league, a win counts 3 points, a loss counts 1 point and a draw counts 2 points. If the results matrix is premultiplied by (3 1 2), a new matrix is obtained.

$$\text{Points} \overset{W \quad L \quad D}{\begin{pmatrix} 3 & 1 & 2 \end{pmatrix}} \begin{array}{c} W \\ L \\ D \end{array} \overset{1st\ 2nd\ 3rd\ Jun}{\begin{pmatrix} 9 & 3 & 4 & 6 \\ 5 & 4 & 4 & 0 \\ 2 & 3 & 1 & 3 \end{pmatrix}} = \text{Points} \overset{1st \quad 2nd \quad 3rd \quad Jun}{\begin{pmatrix} 36 & 19 & 18 & 24 \end{pmatrix}}$$

The new matrix shows the total points gained by each team, e.g. 1st team 36 points, etc.

If, instead, the results matrix were premultiplied by (1 1 1) what information would the new matrix give?

---

e.g. (2) The Walker family buy bottles of milk, tubs of cream and cartons of yogurt from the milkman. The items they bought last week can be shown as a 3 x 6 matrix

(M=Monday, etc.)

$$\begin{array}{r} \\ \text{Milk} \\ \text{Cream} \\ \text{Yogurt} \end{array} \begin{array}{c} \begin{array}{cccccc} M & Tu & W & Th & F & S \end{array} \\ \begin{pmatrix} 4 & 3 & 3 & 2 & 4 & 6 \\ 2 & 0 & 2 & 0 & 1 & 2 \\ 8 & 4 & 6 & 4 & 0 & 10 \end{pmatrix} \end{array}$$

This matrix shows that on Monday the Walkers bought 4 bottles of milk, 2 tubs of cream and 8 cartons of yogurt, etc.

Milk costs 30p a bottle, cream costs 42p a tub and yogurt costs 25p a carton. Premultiplying by (30 42 25) gives the total cost, in pence, for each day's supply

$$\begin{pmatrix} 30 & 42 & 25 \end{pmatrix} \begin{pmatrix} 4 & 3 & 3 & 2 & 4 & 6 \\ 2 & 0 & 2 & 0 & 1 & 2 \\ 8 & 4 & 6 & 4 & 0 & 10 \end{pmatrix} = \begin{pmatrix} 404 & 190 & 324 & 160 & 162 & 514 \end{pmatrix}$$

What information would be given by multiplying the following matrices?

$$\begin{pmatrix} 404 & 190 & 324 & 160 & 162 & 514 \end{pmatrix} \begin{pmatrix} 1 \\ 1 \\ 1 \\ 1 \\ 1 \\ 1 \end{pmatrix}$$

a

1) (a) At an athletics meeting, Spilman Street School gained 5 first places, 6 seconds and 3 thirds. Lowe Road School gained 4 firsts, 8 seconds and 2 thirds. Write this information as a 3 x 2 matrix P.
(b) There are 5 points for a first, 3 for a second and 1 for a third. Write this as a 1 x 3 matrix Q.
(c) Multiply QP to see which school won.

---

2) A hotel offers three classes of accommodation: A, B and C. During a certain month the number of guests and class of accommodation chosen were: Week 1, 9 class A, 6 class B, 3 class C; week 2. 10A, 2B, 5C; week 3, 6A, 4B, 6C; week 4, 6A, 5B, 7C.
(i) Write this information as a 3 x 4 matrix N.
(ii) Class A costs £14 a week, B costs £22 and C costs £27. Write this information as a 1 x 3 matrix M.
(iii) Multiply MN and explain what information the answer gives.

---

3) (a) During a series of rugby matches the 1st XV scored 12 tries, 5 goals and 6 conversions. The 2nd XV scored 10 tries, 3 goals and 4 conversions. Write these results as a 2 x 3 matrix A.
(b) A try gains 4 points, a goal 3 points and a conversion 2 points. Write this as a 3 x 1 matrix B.
(c) Multiply AB and explain what the answer means.

---

4) (a) A tollbridge charges for each vehicle which uses it. The charge is £2 for a car, £1 for a motorcycle and £4 for a lorry or bus. Write these charges as a 1 x 3 matrix C.
(b) On a certain day 433 cars, 28 motorcycles and 174 lorries and buses pass over the bridge. Write these figures as a 3 x 1 matrix D.
(c) Multiply CD and say what the answer means.
(d) E is the matrix $\begin{pmatrix} 1 & 1 & 1 \end{pmatrix}$. Multiply ED and say what the answer means.

---

5) (a) At the sweet shop, Ben bought 3 toffee bars, 5 lollies and 12 fruit sweets; Lucy bought 4 toffee bars, 3 lollies and 7 fruit sweets. Write this information as a 2 x 3 matrix K.
(b) Toffee bars are 11p each, lollies 6p each and fruit sweets 3p each. Write this as a 3 x 1 matrix L.
(c) Multiply KL to give M. What information does M show?
(d) Premultiply M by the matrix $\begin{pmatrix} \frac{1}{2} & \frac{1}{2} \end{pmatrix}$ to give N, and explain what information N gives.

A MATRICES (7)

Matrix transformations

Certain matrices can be used to show transformations (reflections or rotations),

e.g. 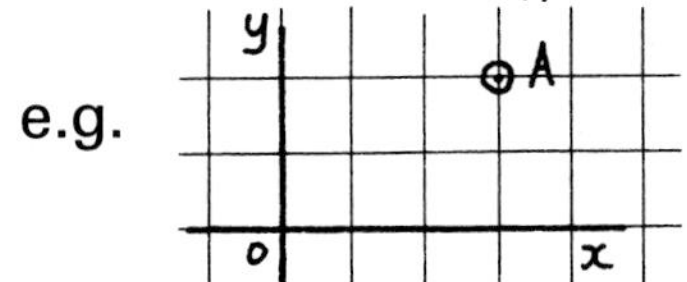

The point A in the drawing has coordinates (3, 2)

The coordinates of A may also be written as a matrix $\begin{pmatrix} 3 \\ 2 \end{pmatrix}$. By premultiplying by the matrix $\begin{pmatrix} 1 & 0 \\ 0 & -1 \end{pmatrix}$ a new matrix is formed $\begin{pmatrix} 1 & 0 \\ 0 & -1 \end{pmatrix}\begin{pmatrix} 3 \\ 2 \end{pmatrix} = \begin{pmatrix} 3 \\ -2 \end{pmatrix}$

The new matrix represents a new point with coordinates (3, –2)

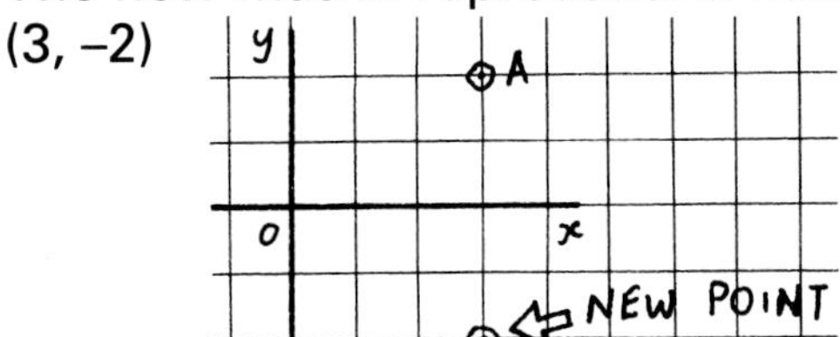

The new point is the reflection of A in the x axis.

e.g. (2) The corners of a triangle PQR have coordinates P (1, 1), Q (2, 1), R (1, 3). Write these coordinates as a 2 x 3 matrix. Then premultiply the matrix by $\begin{pmatrix} -1 & 0 \\ 0 & -1 \end{pmatrix}$

From your answer, describe how the triangle PQR has been transformed. $\begin{pmatrix} -1 & 0 \\ 0 & -1 \end{pmatrix}\begin{pmatrix} 1 & 2 & 1 \\ 1 & 1 & 3 \end{pmatrix} = \begin{pmatrix} -1 & -2 & -1 \\ -1 & -1 & -3 \end{pmatrix}$

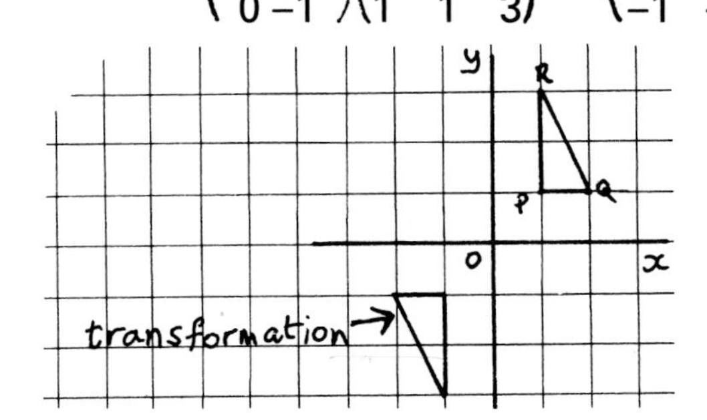

Triangle PQR has been rotated 180° about 0.

a

Use squared paper to answer these questions (1cm squares are probably best). For each question, first draw x and y axes from –6 to +6 each.

1) Plot points A (5, 2), B (1, 4), C (1, 2). Join the points to form a triangle. Write these coordinates as a 2 x 3 matrix and premultiply by $\begin{pmatrix} -1 & 0 \\ 0 & 1 \end{pmatrix}$.
Plot the new points to show the image of ABC.
Describe in words how ABC has been transformed.

2) Plot points J (3, 5), K (2, 5), L(2 ,2), M(5, 2) and join to form a quadrilateral. Write the coordinates as a 2 x 4 matrix and pre multiply by $\begin{pmatrix} 0 & 1 \\ -1 & 0 \end{pmatrix}$.
Plot the quadrilateral which is the image of JKLM and describe the transformation which JKLM has undergone.

3) Plot points D (4, 1), E (4, 4), F (6, 2). Join these points to form a triangle DEF. Write the coordinates as a matrix and pre multiply by $\begin{pmatrix} 0 & 1 \\ 1 & 0 \end{pmatrix}$.
Plot the coordinates given by your answer and join to form a triangle. What is the graph of the line in which DEF is reflected?

4) Repeat question 3, using the same axes, but premultiply instead by $\begin{pmatrix} 0 & -1 \\ -1 & 0 \end{pmatrix}$. Describe this transformation.

5) Draw a triangle with corners (–1, 4), (–5, 2), (–3, 2) and write these coordinates as a matrix. Premultiply by $\begin{pmatrix} 0 & -1 \\ 1 & 0 \end{pmatrix}$ and plot the position of the new triangle given by your answer.

6) Plot points (–2, –1), (–4, –1), (–2, –2) to form a triangle A. Arrange the coordinates as a 2 x 3 matrix and premultiply by $\begin{pmatrix} 1 & 0 \\ 0 & -1 \end{pmatrix}$.
Draw the new triangle B.
What transformation does $\begin{pmatrix} 1 & 0 \\ 0 & -1 \end{pmatrix}$ represent?

7) Repeat question 6, using the same axes, but premultiply instead by $\begin{pmatrix} -1 & 0 \\ 0 & -1 \end{pmatrix}$. Describe this transformation.

8) Draw triangle P = $\begin{pmatrix} 2 & 4 & 2 \\ -5 & -4 & -4 \end{pmatrix}$. Premultiply by M = $\begin{pmatrix} 0 & -1 \\ 1 & 0 \end{pmatrix}$ to give Q. Draw the triangle represented by Q. Premultiply Q by N $\begin{pmatrix} 0 & 1 \\ 1 & 0 \end{pmatrix}$ to give R. Draw the triangle represented by R.
By multiplying NM find the single matrix which maps P on to R. Describe the transformations P to Q, Q to R, P to R.

9) Draw triangle P (2, 1), Q (3, 1), R (3, 3) and write as a 2 x 3 matrix. Premultiply by $\begin{pmatrix} 2 & 0 \\ 0 & 2 \end{pmatrix}$ and draw the result.
(a) How does the length of the new figure compare with the original?
(b) How does the area of the new figure compare with the original?
(c) What is this kind of transformation called?

10) Draw a figure with any coordinates. Write these in matrix form and premultiply by $\begin{pmatrix} 1 & 1 \\ 1 & 1 \end{pmatrix}$.
What is the graph of the line produced by your answer?

A VECTORS (1)

A VECTOR is the movement of a point in a straight line from one position to another. A vector has **size** (usually called MAGNITUDE or LENGTH) and **direction.**

e.g.

The vector $\overrightarrow{PQ}$ is the movement of a point 5 units **along** (parallel to the x axis). It can be written as a column matrix (also called a column vector)

$$\overrightarrow{PQ} = \begin{pmatrix}5\\0\end{pmatrix}$$

The vector QR is the movement of a point 3 units **up** (parallel to the y axis). It is written

$$\overrightarrow{QR} = \begin{pmatrix}0\\3\end{pmatrix}$$

When two vectors are **added together,** they make a new vector,

e.g.

$$\overrightarrow{PR} = \overrightarrow{PQ} + \overrightarrow{QR}$$

$$= \begin{pmatrix}5\\0\end{pmatrix}+\begin{pmatrix}0\\3\end{pmatrix}$$

$$\overrightarrow{PR} = \begin{pmatrix}5\\3\end{pmatrix}$$

In this drawing, $\overrightarrow{PQ}$ and $\overrightarrow{QR}$ are COMPONENT vectors and $\overrightarrow{PR}$ is the RESULTANT vector.

The vector $\overrightarrow{RP} = \begin{pmatrix}-5\\-3\end{pmatrix}$. It has the same magnitude as $\overrightarrow{PR}$ but goes in the opposite direction.

Vectors are shown in writing
either (1) as two letters with an arrow on top, e.g. $\overrightarrow{AB}$
or (2) as a small letter, e.g. **a**

Vectors are shown in drawings as straight lines with arrows on them

e.g.

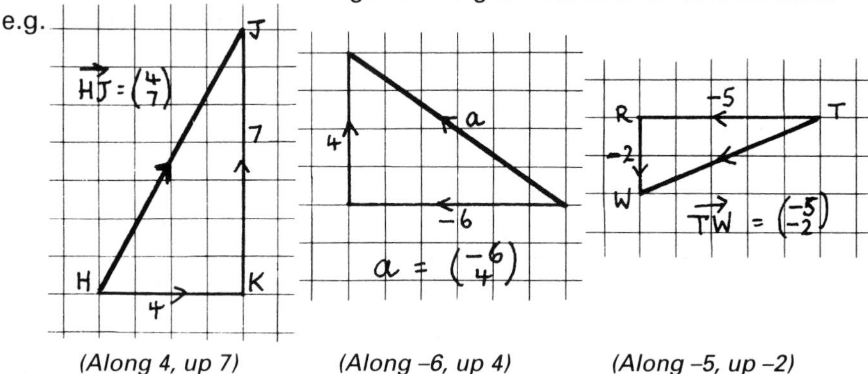

(Along 4, up 7) *(Along –6, up 4)* *(Along –5, up –2)*

a On squared paper (1 cm squares are probably best) draw these vectors. Remember to put an arrow to show the direction of each vector.

1) $\vec{AB} = \begin{pmatrix}6\\0\end{pmatrix}$
2) $\vec{MN} = \begin{pmatrix}2\\0\end{pmatrix}$
3) $\vec{XY} = \begin{pmatrix}4\\0\end{pmatrix}$
4) $\vec{TV} = \begin{pmatrix}-5\\0\end{pmatrix}$
5) $\vec{DG} = \begin{pmatrix}0\\3\end{pmatrix}$
6) $\vec{KM} = \begin{pmatrix}0\\7\end{pmatrix}$
7) $\vec{HN} = \begin{pmatrix}0\\4\end{pmatrix}$
8) $\vec{CA} = \begin{pmatrix}-1\\0\end{pmatrix}$
9) $\vec{WV} = \begin{pmatrix}0\\9\end{pmatrix}$
10) $\vec{EF} = \begin{pmatrix}0\\-6\end{pmatrix}$

b Add each pair of vectors. Write the answers as a new vector and draw a diagram showing the component vectors and the resultant vector.

1) $\begin{pmatrix}4\\0\end{pmatrix}+\begin{pmatrix}0\\3\end{pmatrix}$
2) $\begin{pmatrix}5\\0\end{pmatrix}+\begin{pmatrix}0\\6\end{pmatrix}$
3) $\begin{pmatrix}3\\0\end{pmatrix}+\begin{pmatrix}0\\-5\end{pmatrix}$
4) $\begin{pmatrix}-7\\0\end{pmatrix}+\begin{pmatrix}0\\4\end{pmatrix}$
5) $\begin{pmatrix}-6\\0\end{pmatrix}+\begin{pmatrix}0\\-4\end{pmatrix}$

c Draw these vectors on squared paper

1) $a = \begin{pmatrix}6\\2\end{pmatrix}$
2) $\vec{LM} = \begin{pmatrix}1\\7\end{pmatrix}$
3) $c = \begin{pmatrix}5\\5\end{pmatrix}$
4) $b = \begin{pmatrix}4\\-2\end{pmatrix}$
5) $\vec{RP} = \begin{pmatrix}-4\\3\end{pmatrix}$
6) $h = \begin{pmatrix}2\\8\end{pmatrix}$
7) $\vec{JK} = \begin{pmatrix}-2\\-5\end{pmatrix}$
8) $m = \begin{pmatrix}-6\\9\end{pmatrix}$
9) $\vec{XZ} = \begin{pmatrix}-1\\-7\end{pmatrix}$
10) $q = \begin{pmatrix}3\\-4\end{pmatrix}$

d Write down the column vector represented by each of these

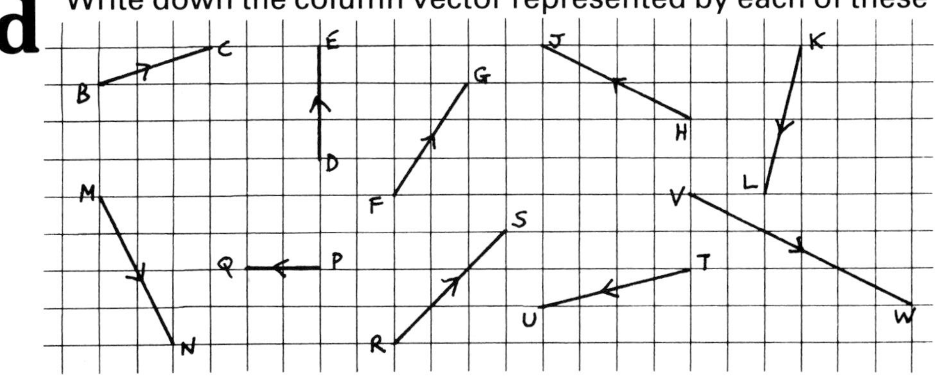

A VECTORS (2)

Addition of 'sloping' vectors

e.g. Add the vectors $\begin{pmatrix}2\\4\end{pmatrix}$ and $\begin{pmatrix}6\\1\end{pmatrix}$. Write the answer as a new column vector and draw a diagram to represent the sum.

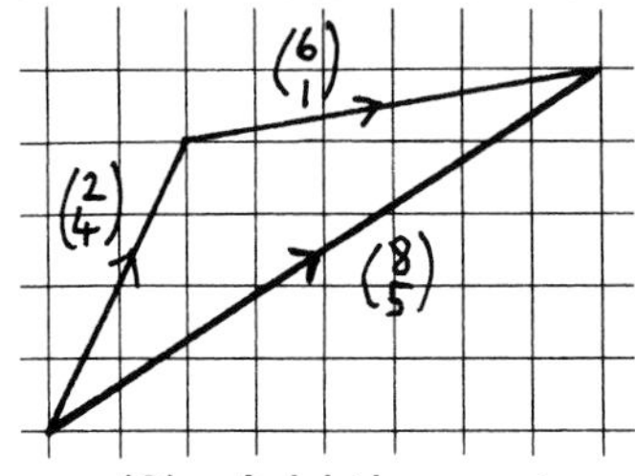

$\begin{pmatrix}2\\4\end{pmatrix} + \begin{pmatrix}6\\1\end{pmatrix} = \begin{pmatrix}8\\5\end{pmatrix}$

$\begin{pmatrix}2\\4\end{pmatrix}$ and $\begin{pmatrix}6\\1\end{pmatrix}$ are the component vectors and $\begin{pmatrix}8\\5\end{pmatrix}$ is the resultant vector.

e.g. (2) Add the vectors $\vec{KL} = \begin{pmatrix}-3\\1\end{pmatrix}$ and $\vec{LM} = \begin{pmatrix}5\\-4\end{pmatrix}$

$\vec{KL} + \vec{LM} = \begin{pmatrix}-3\\1\end{pmatrix} + \begin{pmatrix}5\\-4\end{pmatrix} = \begin{pmatrix}2\\-3\end{pmatrix}$

The result of adding $\vec{KL}$ and $\vec{LM}$ is a new vector $\vec{KM} = \begin{pmatrix}2\\-3\end{pmatrix}$

B

Arrow direction in vector triangles

In a vector triangle, the arrow on the resultant vector goes round the triangle the opposite way to the arrows on the component vectors.

e.g. In the triangle PQR, which is the resultant vector?

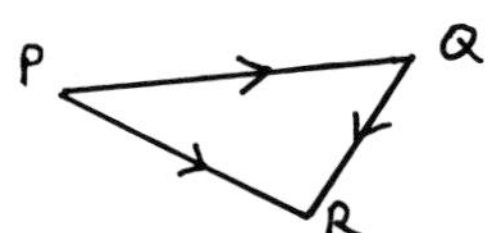

The arrows on $\vec{PQ}$ and $\vec{QR}$ go clockwise. The arrow on $\vec{PR}$ goes anticlockwise (the opposite way), so **$\vec{PR}$ is the resultant vector.**

The resultant is the direct route (short cut) from start to finish. It is often marked with TWO arrows to make it clear.

Vector addition, subtraction and multiplication

e.g. If a is the vector $\begin{pmatrix}3\\4\end{pmatrix}$, b is the vector $\begin{pmatrix}2\\-1\end{pmatrix}$

the vector 2a is $2\begin{pmatrix}3\\4\end{pmatrix} = \begin{pmatrix}6\\8\end{pmatrix}$

the vector 3b is $3\begin{pmatrix}2\\-1\end{pmatrix} = \begin{pmatrix}6\\-3\end{pmatrix}$

the vector a + 2b is $\begin{pmatrix}3\\4\end{pmatrix} + \begin{pmatrix}4\\-2\end{pmatrix} = \begin{pmatrix}7\\2\end{pmatrix}$

the vector b − a is $\begin{pmatrix}2\\-1\end{pmatrix} - \begin{pmatrix}3\\4\end{pmatrix} = \begin{pmatrix}-1\\-5\end{pmatrix}$ etc.

a Add each pair of vectors. Write the answer as a new column vector. Then draw a diagram, showing the component vectors and the resultant vector. Make sure arrows are facing the correct ways.

1) $\begin{pmatrix}4\\1\end{pmatrix} + \begin{pmatrix}2\\2\end{pmatrix}$
2) $\begin{pmatrix}5\\2\end{pmatrix} + \begin{pmatrix}1\\3\end{pmatrix}$
3) $\begin{pmatrix}3\\3\end{pmatrix} + \begin{pmatrix}0\\2\end{pmatrix}$
4) $\begin{pmatrix}3\\2\end{pmatrix} + \begin{pmatrix}4\\1\end{pmatrix}$
5) $\begin{pmatrix}2\\2\end{pmatrix} + \begin{pmatrix}-4\\2\end{pmatrix}$
6) $\begin{pmatrix}1\\5\end{pmatrix} + \begin{pmatrix}4\\0\end{pmatrix}$
7) $\begin{pmatrix}-2\\2\end{pmatrix} + \begin{pmatrix}6\\1\end{pmatrix}$
8) $\begin{pmatrix}2\\-3\end{pmatrix} + \begin{pmatrix}-4\\-2\end{pmatrix}$
9) $\begin{pmatrix}-3\\3\end{pmatrix} + \begin{pmatrix}2\\-5\end{pmatrix}$
10) $\begin{pmatrix}3\\4\end{pmatrix} + \begin{pmatrix}1\\4\end{pmatrix}$
11) $\begin{pmatrix}0\\-3\end{pmatrix} + \begin{pmatrix}3\\5\end{pmatrix}$
12) $\begin{pmatrix}-3\\2\end{pmatrix} + \begin{pmatrix}3\\-7\end{pmatrix}$
13) $\begin{pmatrix}4\\-2\end{pmatrix} + \begin{pmatrix}-5\\8\end{pmatrix}$
14) $\begin{pmatrix}-3\\-1\end{pmatrix} + \begin{pmatrix}5\\5\end{pmatrix}$
15) $\begin{pmatrix}9\\2\end{pmatrix} + \begin{pmatrix}-4\\-4\end{pmatrix}$

b Write down which is the resultant vector in each of these

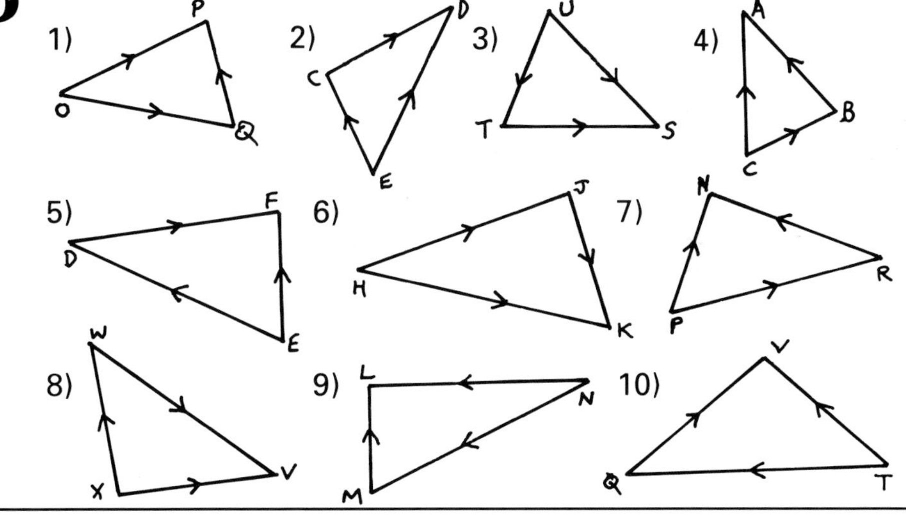

c If $a = \begin{pmatrix}3\\1\end{pmatrix}$, $b = \begin{pmatrix}1\\-1\end{pmatrix}$, $c = \begin{pmatrix}-2\\3\end{pmatrix}$, work out these and write them as column vectors.

1) 2a
2) 3b
3) 5c
4) a + b
5) b + c
6) a – c
7) 2b + a
8) 2c + 4b
9) 3a + c
10) –4b
11) 2b – 3c
12) c – b
13) a + b + c
14) 4c – 2a
15) 5b + 2c

A VECTORS (3)

Drawing + − x of vectors

e.g. a is the vector $\begin{pmatrix}1\\2\end{pmatrix}$, b is the vector $\begin{pmatrix}3\\-1\end{pmatrix}$

$\overrightarrow{HJ} = 2a$, $\overrightarrow{HK} = b$. (i) Draw the vectors $\overrightarrow{HJ}$, $\overrightarrow{HK}$ and $\overrightarrow{JK}$.

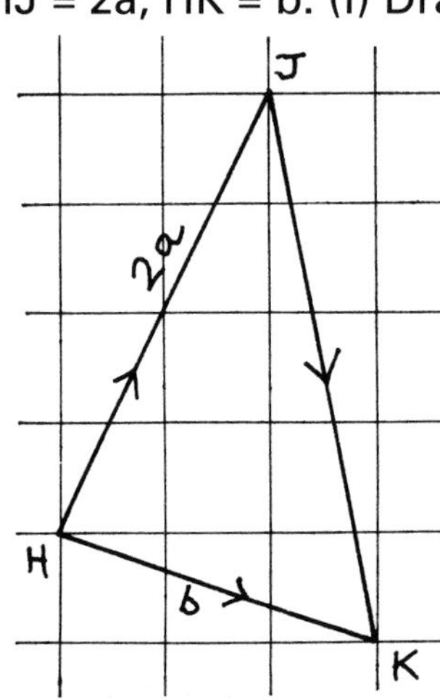

$\overrightarrow{HJ} = 2\begin{pmatrix}1\\2\end{pmatrix} = \begin{pmatrix}2\\4\end{pmatrix}$, $\overrightarrow{HK} = \begin{pmatrix}3\\-1\end{pmatrix}$

(ii) Express $\overrightarrow{JK}$ as a column vector.
From the drawing, $\overrightarrow{JK} = \begin{pmatrix}1\\-5\end{pmatrix}$

(iii) Express $\overrightarrow{JK}$ in terms of a and b.
In the vector triangle the resultant vector is $\overrightarrow{HK}$ (Its arrow goes the opposite way to the others),
so $\overrightarrow{HK} = \overrightarrow{HJ} + \overrightarrow{JK}$
which, when rearranged, becomes
$\overrightarrow{JK} = \overrightarrow{HK} - \overrightarrow{HJ}$
so $\overrightarrow{JK} = b - 2a$

B Magnitude of a vector

The MAGNITUDE (or LENGTH) of a 'horizontal' or 'vertical' vector, i.e. one whose column vector contains a zero, can be drawn and measured simply, e.g.

Vector $\overrightarrow{RS} = \begin{pmatrix}5\\0\end{pmatrix}$ Vector $\overrightarrow{DC} = \begin{pmatrix}0\\-3\end{pmatrix}$

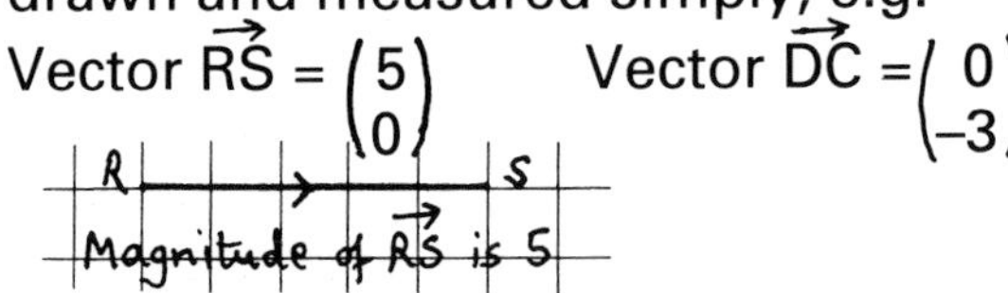

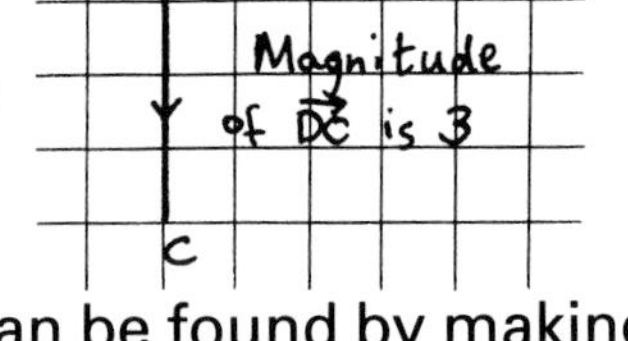

The magnitude of a 'sloping' vector can be found by making the vector the hypotenuse of a right-angled triangle and using Pythagoras' theorem (see page 4),
e.g. vector $\overrightarrow{GJ} = \begin{pmatrix}4\\2\end{pmatrix}$

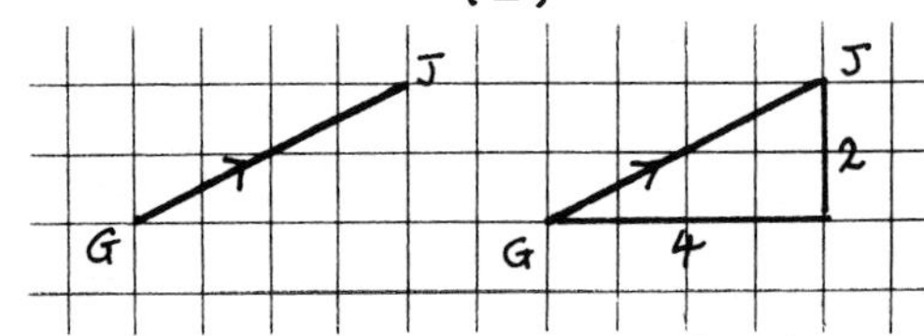

By Pythagoras
$(\text{Mag } \overrightarrow{GJ})^2 = 4^2 + 2^2$
$(\text{Mag } \overrightarrow{GJ})^2 = 16 + 4$
$\text{Mag } \overrightarrow{GJ} = \sqrt{20}$

When working out magnitude, the direction of the vector does not matter. The magnitude of a vector is NEVER negative.

a 1) $a = \begin{pmatrix}3\\1\end{pmatrix}$, $b = \begin{pmatrix}1\\2\end{pmatrix}$. $\vec{OQ} = 2a$, $\vec{QR} = 3b$. Draw $\vec{OQ}$, $\vec{QR}$ and $\vec{OR}$. (a) Write down $\vec{OR}$ (i) as a column vector (ii) in terms of a and b. (b) Write $\vec{RQ}$ as a column vector.

2) $c = \begin{pmatrix}1\\-1\end{pmatrix}$, $d = \begin{pmatrix}2\\1\end{pmatrix}$. $\vec{KL} = 3c$, $\vec{KM} = 2d$. Draw $\vec{KL}$, $\vec{KM}$ and $\vec{LM}$. (a) Write $\vec{LM}$ as a column vector. (b) Which of the three vectors is the resultant vector? (c) Write $\vec{LM}$ in terms of c and d.

3) $a = \begin{pmatrix}2\\3\end{pmatrix}$, $b = \begin{pmatrix}2\\-2\end{pmatrix}$. $\vec{OT} = a$, $\vec{TU} = 2b$, $\vec{UV} = -2a$
Draw $\vec{OT}$, $\vec{TU}$, $\vec{UV}$ and $\vec{OV}$. (i) Write $\vec{OV}$ as a column vector. (ii) Write $\vec{OV}$ in terms of a and b. (iii) Write $\vec{OU}$ in terms of a and b.

4) $\vec{PQ} = \begin{pmatrix}3\\3\end{pmatrix}$, $\vec{PR} = \begin{pmatrix}4\\-4\end{pmatrix}$. If $a = \begin{pmatrix}1\\1\end{pmatrix}$, $b = \begin{pmatrix}1\\-1\end{pmatrix}$, express $\vec{PQ}$, $\vec{PR}$ and $\vec{QR}$ in terms of a and b.

5) $a = \begin{pmatrix}1\\3\end{pmatrix}$, $b = \begin{pmatrix}2\\1\end{pmatrix}$. Draw $\vec{FH} = a$, $\vec{FG} = -2b$, $\vec{GJ} = 2a$.
(a) Write $\vec{JH}$ (i) as a column vector (ii) in terms of a and b.
(b) Write $\vec{FJ}$ (i) as a column vector (ii) in terms of a and b.

---

b 1) Find the magnitude of each of these vectors. Answers may be left as square roots or given correct to 2 significant figures.

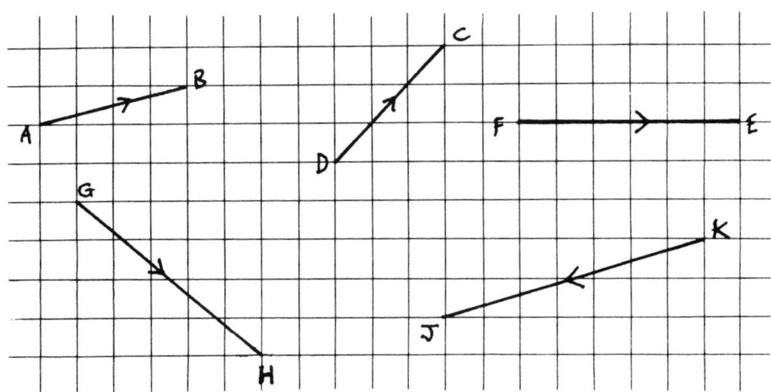

2) $a = \begin{pmatrix}4\\1\end{pmatrix}$, $b = \begin{pmatrix}3\\3\end{pmatrix}$. On squared paper, draw $\vec{PS} = b$, $\vec{SR} = b$, $\vec{PQ} = 2a$. Then work out the magnitude of $\vec{PS}$, $\vec{PR}$, $\vec{PQ}$, $\vec{SQ}$ and $\vec{RQ}$. Answers may be left as square roots or given correct to 2 significant figures.

MULTIPLICATION OF TWO BRACKETS

When two brackets are multiplied out, everything in the first bracket must be multiplied by everything in the second bracket,

e.g. Multiply out $(x + 2)(x - 3)$

***F**irsts*	$(\underline{x} + 2)(\underline{x} - 3)$	$x \times x$	$= x^2$
***O**utsides*	$(\underline{x} + 2)(x \underline{-3})$	$x \times -3$	$= -3x$
***I**nsides*	$(x \underline{+2})(\underline{x} - 3)$	$2 \times x$	$= +2x$
***L**asts*	$(x + \underline{2})(x \underline{-3})$	2×-3	$= -6$

$$x^2 - 3x + 2x - 6$$

$$= x^2 - x - 6$$

The answer is an expression with three terms and is called a TRINOMIAL.

---

e.g. (2) $(x + 4)(2x + 1)$

$$x \times 2x = 2x^2$$
$$x \times 1 = +x$$
$$4 \times 2x = +8x$$
$$4 \times 1 = +4$$

$$2x^2 + x + 8x + 4$$

$$= 2x^2 + 9x + 4$$

It is usual to write the terms in DESCENDING POWERS - **first** x^2 terms, **then** x terms, **then** ordinary numbers

---

e.g. (3) $(x - 5)^2 = (x - 5)(x - 5) = x^2 - 5x - 5x + 25$

$$= x^2 - 10x + 25$$

e.g. (4) $2(3x + 1)(x - 4) = 2(3x^2 - 11x - 4) = 6x^2 - 22x - 8$

e.g. (5) $(x - 2y)(2x - y) = 2x^2 - xy - 4xy + 2y^2$

$$= 2x^2 - 5xy + 2y^2$$

e.g. (6) $(4 + 7)(1 + 5) = 4 + 20 + 7 + 35 = 66$

e.g. (7) $(x + 3)(x - 3) = x^2 - 3x + 3x - 9 = x^2 - 9$

Example (7) is called the DIFFERENCE OF TWO SQUARES (x squared subtract 9 squared).

a

Multiply out

1) $(x + 3)(x + 4)$
2) $(x + 1)(x + 5)$
3) $(x + 6)(x + 2)$
4) $(x + 3)(x - 2)$
5) $(x - 5)(x + 5)$
6) $(x + 8)(x + 1)$
7) $(x - 4)(x - 2)$
8) $(x + 7)(x - 3)$
9) $(x + 4)(x + 4)$
10) $(x - 5)(x - 6)$

---

b

Multiply out

1) $(x - 12)(x - 1)$
2) $(2x + 3)(x + 2)$
3) $(x + 5)(x + 8)$
4) $(3x + 1)(x - 1)$
5) $(x - 7)(x - 4)$
6) $(x + \frac{1}{2})(x + \frac{1}{2})$
7) $(2x + 1)(2x + 2)$
8) $(x - 3)(3x - 1)$
9) $(6 + 2)(4 + 3)$
10) $(4x + 1)(2x - 5)$

---

c

Multiply out

1) $(x + 5)^2$
2) $(x - 2)^2$
3) $(x + 4)^2$
4) $(x + 3)^2$
5) $(x + y)^2$
6) $(x - y)^2$
7) $(x - 6)^2$
8) $(2x + 3)^2$
9) $(x - 9)^2$
10) $(3x + 4)^2$

---

d

Multiply out

1) $(x + 2)(x - 2)$
2) $(x + 4)(x - 4)$
3) $(x + y)(x - y)$
4) $(x + 6)(x - 6)$
5) $(x - 10)(x + 10)$
6) $(2x + 1)(2x - 1)$
7) $(x + 7)(x - 7)$
8) $(3x + 2)(3x - 2)$
9) $(7 + 3)(7 - 3)$
10) $(5x - 8)(5x + 8)$

---

e

Multiply out

1) $2(x - 1)(x + 3)$
2) $4(x + 2)(x + 4)$
3) $3(2x - 1)(x + 2)$
4) $6(x - 2)(x - 3)$
5) $4(x + y)(x + y)$
6) $5(x + 1)(x + 5)$
7) $2(x + 3)(3x - 4)$
8) $8(x - 2)(x - 1)$
9) $3(2x - 3)(2x + 3)$
10) $\frac{1}{2}(x - 6)(2x - 4)$

A FACTORISATION (1)

Factorising trinomials

When a trinomial of the type $Ax^2 + Bx + C$ is factorised, the result is the product of two brackets, e.g.

$$x^2 + 7x + 10 = (x + 2)(x + 5)$$

This is the opposite operation to Multiplication of Two Brackets on page 32.

* 1) Look at signs

$x^2 + Bx + C$	will give	$(x + \quad)(x + \quad)$
$x^2 - Bx + C$	will give	$(x - \quad)(x - \quad)$
$x^2 + Bx - C$	will give either	$(x + \quad)(x - \quad)$
and $x^2 - Bx - C$	or	$(x - \quad)(x + \quad)$

* 2) To find the second number in each bracket if the last term is **+**, e.g. $x^2 + 7x + 12$, find the **factors** of the last term which **ADD** to give the coefficient of the middle term.

$$x^2 \quad \underset{(4+3)}{+7x} \quad \underset{(4 \times 3)}{+12} = (x + 4)(x + 3)$$

e.g. $$a^2 \quad \underset{(7+2)}{-9a} \quad \underset{(7 \times 2)}{+14} = (a - 7)(a - 2)$$

To find the second number in each bracket if the last term is **–**, e.g. $x^2 + 4x - 12$, find the **factors** of the last term which **SUBTRACT** to give the coefficient of the middle term.

e.g. * $$x^2 \quad \underset{(6-2)}{+4x} \quad \underset{(6 \times 2)}{-12} = (x + 6)(x - 2)$$

* $$x^2 \quad \underset{(6-2)}{-4x} \quad \underset{(6 \times 2)}{-12} = (x - 6)(x + 2)$$

* Notice the different answers given by these two examples. If the original middle term is +, the larger number in brackets is +, e.g.

$$n^2 + 2n - 15 = (n + 5)(n - 3)$$

If the original middle term is –, the larger number in brackets is –, e.g.

$$n^2 - 2n - 15 = (n - 5)(n + 3)$$

When factorising, always find the highest factor common to all terms first, e.g. Factorise $2x^2 - 6x - 20$

All the terms divide by 2, so take the factor of 2 out first, and then continue as before.

$$2x^2 - 6x - 20$$
$$2(x^2 - 3x - 10)$$
$$2(x - 5)(x + 2)$$

a

Factorise into two brackets

1) $x^2 + 5x + 6$
2) $x^2 + 7x + 6$
3) $x^2 + 2x + 1$
4) $p^2 + 10p + 16$
5) $c^2 + 11c + 18$
6) $x^2 + 9x + 20$
7) $y^2 + 4y + 4$
8) $x^2 - 5x + 4$
9) $m^2 - 7m + 10$
10) $x^2 - 2x + 1$
11) $x^2 - 5x + 6$
12) $a^2 - 10a + 21$
13) $x^2 + 8x + 16$
14) $h^2 + 6h + 8$
15) $x^2 - 13x + 12$

---

b

Factorise into two brackets

1) $x^2 + x - 2$
2) $x^2 - 3x - 18$
3) $x^2 + 8x - 9$
4) $x^2 - 6x + 9$
5) $x^2 - 4x - 5$
6) $x^2 - 10x + 25$
7) $x^2 + x - 6$
8) $x^2 + 11x + 28$
9) $x^2 - 12x + 11$
10) $x^2 + 5x - 24$
11) $x^2 + 8x + 12$
12) $x^2 - 5x - 14$
13) $x^2 + 2x - 3$
14) $x^2 - 9x + 14$
15) $x^2 + x - 20$

---

c

Factorise into two brackets

1) $x^2 + 25x + 24$
2) $x^2 - 18x + 80$
3) $x^2 - 20x + 100$
4) $x^2 + 2xy + y^2$
5) $x^2 - 14x - 32$
6) $x^2 + x + \frac{1}{4}$
7) $x^2 + 18x + 45$
8) $25 + 60 + 36$
9) $x^2 + 2x - 8$
10) $x^2 - 6x - 7$
11) $x^2 + 19x + 60$
12) $x^2 + 8x - 33$
13) $49 - 42 + 9$
14) $2x^2 + 3x + 1$
15) $10x^2 + 41x + 40$

---

d

Factorise. In each example, first find the highest factor common to all the terms. Then factorise into brackets.

1) $3x^2 + 15x + 18$
2) $2x^2 + 4x - 30$
3) $7x^2 - 7x - 14$
4) $4x^2 + 28x + 48$
5) $2x^2 - 10x + 8$
6) $5x^2 + 10x + 5$
7) $6x^2 - 30x - 84$
8) $4x^2 - 26x + 12$
9) $x^3 + 6x^2 + 5x$
10) $3x^2 + 27x - 30$

A FACTORISATION (2)

Difference of two squares

* The difference of two squares is factorised as
square root of first square + square root of second square
multiplied by
square root of first square – square root of second square

e.g. $x^2 - y^2 = (x + y)\ (x - y)$
$n^2 - 9 = (n + 3)\ (n - 3)$
$4a^2 - 25b^2 = (2a + 5b)\ (2a - 5b)$

This method can be used for problems without letters
e.g.

$$81 - 16 = (9 + 4)(9 - 4) = 13 \times 5 = 65$$
$$100^2 - 99^2 = (100 + 99)\ (100 - 99) = 199 \times 1 = 199$$
$$(22.6)^2 - (17.4)^2 = (22.6 + 17.4)\ (22.6 - 17.4) = 40 \times 5.2 = 208$$

C

When factorising, always find any factors common to both terms first

e.g. (1) Factorise $8x^2 - 2y^2$
$2(4x^2 - y^2)$
$2(2x + y)\ (2x - y)$

e.g. (2) Factorise $27p^2 - 12q^2$
$3(9p^2 - 4q^2)$
$3(3p + 2q)\ (3p - 2q)$

Factorising expressions with four terms

*First split into two groups of two terms. Then take out common factors, e.g. $bd - be + cd - ce$

$bd - be \quad + cd - ce$
$b(d - e) \quad + c(d - e)$
$(b + c)\ (d - e)$

Sometimes the terms need to be rearranged first,
e.g. (2)

$uv + xy + uy + xv$
$uv + uy \quad + xv + xy$
$u(v + y) \quad +x(v + y)$
$(u + x)\ (v + y)$

e.g. (3)

$fh + gj - gh - fj$
$fh - fj \quad - gh + gj$
$f(h - j) \quad -g(h - j)$
$(f - g)\ (h - j)$

a

Multiply out these brackets (See page 32). Each answer should be a difference of two squares.

1) $(a + b)(a - b)$
2) $(x + 2)(x - 2)$
3) $(4 + y)(4 - y)$
4) $(2x + y)(2x - y)$
5) $(n - 6)(n + 6)$
6) $(5 + 2)(5 - 2)$
7) $(3a - 4b)(3a + 4b)$
8) $(6j + h)(6j - h)$
9) $(2m + 7k)(2m - 7k)$
10) $(x^2 + y)(x^2 - y)$

---

b

Factorise

1) $a^2 - b^2$
2) $x^2 - 4$
3) $9h^2 - j^2$
4) $49 - 36$
5) $64x^2 - 25y^2$
6) $16a^2 - 9b^2$
7) $n^2 - \frac{4}{9}$
8) $144 - 121$
9) $x^6 - 81$
10) $4c^2 - 1$

---

c

Factorise by finding common factors first

1) $2x^2 - 2y^2$
2) $3p^2 - 3q^2$
3) $2m^2 - 8t^2$
4) $18w^2 - 2v^2$
5) $2y^2 - 32$
6) $12d^2 - 27e^2$
7) $75 - 3h^2$
8) $20p^2 - 45n^2$
9) $6j^2 - 24m^2$
10) $8a^2 - 50$

---

d

Find answers to these by factorising the difference of two squares

1) $59^2 - 58^2$
2) $34^2 - 24^2$
3) $201^2 - 199^2$
4) $22^2 - 17^2$
5) $89^2 - 79^2$
6) $19^2 - 16^2$
7) $148^2 - 48^2$
8) $67^2 - 63^2$
9) $59^2 - 41^2$
10) $228^2 - 222^2$
11) $(0.6)^2 - (0.4)^2$
12) $(7.2)^2 - (2.8)^2$
13) $(3.37)^2 - (1.63)^2$
14) $(9.1)^2 - (8.1)^2$
15) $(0.57)^2 - (0.43)^2$

---

e

Factorise each of these into two brackets

1) $ax + ay + bx + by$
2) $cd + gd + ce + ge$
3) $ah - aj + bh - bj$
4) $mp + qn + mn + qp$
5) $st + su + ut + u^2$
6) $km - zw - kw + zm$
7) $2a + bc + ba + 2c$
8) $df - ph + pf - dh$
9) $4xy - 4xz + wy - wz$
10) $cs + pm - ps - cm$

A QUADRATIC EQUATIONS

A QUADRATIC EQUATION is an equation containing a SQUARED term e.g. $x^2 - x - 6 = 0$

There are usually two possible values for the letter.

To solve a quadratic equation e.g. $x^2 - x - 6 = 0$

* 1) Factorise $(x - 3)(x + 2) = 0$

* 2) When the two brackets are multiplied, they make zero, so one of the brackets must equal zero

$x - 3 = 0$ or $x + 2 = 0$

so the solution is $x = 3$ or $x = -2$

e.g. (2)

$$x^2 - 9x + 20 = 0$$
$$(x - 5)(x - 4) = 0$$
$$x = 5 \quad \text{or} \quad x = 4$$

e.g. (3)

$$2x^2 - 5x - 12 = 0$$
$$(x - 4)(2x + 3) = 0$$
$$x = 4 \quad \text{or} \quad x = -1\tfrac{1}{2}$$

B

If the expression to be factorised does not equal 0, change the equation to obtain 0 on the right–hand side, e.g

$$x^2 + 2x = 63$$
$$x^2 + 2x - 63 = 0$$
$$(x + 9)(x - 7) = 0$$
$$x = -9 \quad \text{or} \quad x = 7$$

Using the formula

If a quadratic equation cannot be solved by the method shown in A at the top of this page, the formula can be used.

For the quadratic equation $Ax^2 + Bx + C = 0$

$$x = \frac{-B \pm \sqrt{B^2 - 4AC}}{2A}$$

e.g. Solve the quadratic equation $3x^2 + 4x - 5 = 0$ giving your answer correct to 2 decimal places.

$$(+3)x^2 (+4)x (-5) = 0$$
$$A = 3, \quad B = 4, \quad C = -5$$

so

$$x = \frac{-4 \pm \sqrt{4^2 - (4 \times 3 \times -5)}}{2 \times 3}$$

$$x = \frac{-4 + \sqrt{76}}{6} \qquad x = \frac{-4 - \sqrt{76}}{6}$$

$x = 0.79$ or $x = -2.12$ (2d.p.)

a

Find the possible values of x in each of these

1) $(x-1)(x-2)=0$
2) $(x-5)(x+1)=0$
3) $(x+3)(x+6)=0$
4) $(x-8)(x-4)=0$
5) $(x+11)(x-3)=0$
6) $(2x-3)(x-1)=0$
7) $(x+5)(3x-2)=0$
8) $(x-9)(x+6)=0$
9) $(4x+5)(2x-7)=0$
10) $(x-8)(4x-1)=0$

---

b

Solve these quadratic equations

1) $x^2-5x+6=0$
2) $x^2-6x+5=0$
3) $x^2+2x-3=0$
4) $x^2+12x+35=0$
5) $x^2+x-12=0$
6) $x^2-9x+14=0$
7) $x^2-2x+1=0$
8) $x^2+8x+7=0$
9) $x^2-13x+36=0$
10) $x^2-2x-48=0$
11) $x^2-26x+48=0$
12) $x^2+2x-15=0$
13) $x^2-8x-20=0$
14) $x^2+11x+28=0$
15) $x^2-9x+20=0$

---

c

Solve these quadratic equations

1) $2x^2-11x+12=0$
2) $3x^2+10x-8=0$
3) $x^2+24x-25=0$
4) $2x^2+17x+8=0$
5) $x^2-4x-32=0$
6) $x^2-7x+6=0$
7) $x^2-15x+54=0$
8) $2x^2-9x+7=0$
9) $x^2+2x-63=0$
10) $3x^2+8x+4=0$

---

d

Solve these quadratic equations. Rearrange each one first so that it is in the form $Ax^2 \pm Bx \pm C = 0$

1) $x^2+3x=18$
2) $x^2-8x=20$
3) $x^2-9x=-20$
4) $x^2+4x=12$
5) $x^2+x=6$
6) $x^2+9x=36$
7) $x^2-4x=21$
8) $2x^2-x=1$
9) $x^2-8x=-16$
10) $x^2-x=42$

---

e

Solve these quadratic equations using the formula on page 38 C. Give answers to 2 decimal places. Square roots can be looked up on page 71.

1) $x^2+5x-2=0$
2) $2x^2-4x+1=0$
3) $x^2+2x-6=0$
4) $3x^2-4x-2=0$
5) $x^2-7x+3=0$
6) $2x^2+5x+3=0$
7) $5x^2-10x+4=0$
8) $8x^2-14x-9=0$
9) $2x^2+6x-5=0$
10) $4x^2-7x=1$

A PROBABILITY

Probability is the likelihood that something (called an EVENT) will happen. It is expressed as a quantity between 0 and 1 inclusive. If an event will definitely happen, the probability is 1, e.g. the probability that the month after next April will be next May is 1. If an event will definitely not happen, the probability is 0, e.g. the probability that the Pacific Ocean will dry up today is 0.
If an event is just as likely to happen as not to happen, the probability is $1/2$ (or 0.5), e.g. the probability of a coin landing heads up when I toss it is $1/2$.
Probability is written as either 0, 1, or a fraction or decimal between 0 and 1. If it is written as a fraction, it should be cancelled to its lowest terms.

B The way that an event **does** happen, or the way you wish it to happen is called a SUCCESSFUL (or FAVOURABLE) OUTCOME.
The number of ways an event can happen is called the SAMPLE SPACE.

$$\text{Probability} = \frac{\text{Number of successful outcomes}}{\text{Sample space}}$$

e.g. The probability that a die will fall with ⚃ upwards is $1/6$ because there are 6 different ways the die **can** fall and only 1 way it **does** fall.
e.g. (2) The probability of picking an ace out of a well-shuffled pack of cards is $4/52 = 1/13$ because there are 52 different cards which can be picked but only 4 which are the kind required.

No. of successful outcomes = No. of aces = 4
Sample space = No. of cards = 52
Probability (ace) = $4/52 = 1/13$

If the ace that has been picked is kept out of the pack, what is the probability of picking another ace? Now the sample space is 51 (because there are now only 51 cards left in the pack) and the number of successful outcomes is 3 (because there are now only 3 aces in the pack) so the probability is $3/51 = 1/17$

Events not happening

The probability of an event **not** happening is found by subtracting the probability of its happening from 1, e.g. the probability of a die falling with the ⚂ upwards is $1/6$, so the probability of its **not** falling with the ⚂ upwards is

$$1 - 1/6 = 5/6$$

a

1) Find the probability
   (a) when a die is thrown, that the number facing upwards will be divisible by 3
   (b) when a card is picked from a pack, it will be a 'diamond'
   (c) of the name of a month beginning with a letter A
   (d) that I shall meet a live dinosaur tomorrow
   (e) that, if I cut out the letters of the word LOLLIPOP, and mix them up in a box, I shall pick a letter L out of the box
2) A red die and a green die are thrown together. Copy and complete this table to find all the different combinations of score

RED DIE	1	1		
GREEN DIE	1	2		
TOTAL SCORE (red + green)	2	3		etc.

3) From your answer to question 2, find the probability that the total score will be
   (i) 5 (ii) 11 (iii) 1 (iv) 7 (v) 4
4) (i) If two coins are tossed, what is the probability of both coins landing heads up?
   (ii) What is the probability of the coins landing with one head and one tail facing upwards?
5) There are 10 red sweets, 8 yellow sweets and 7 green sweets in a bag
   (a) What is the sample space (the total number of sweets)?
   (b) If I dip into the bag without looking, what is the probability of picking a red sweet?
   (c) If I eat the red sweet I have picked, what is now the probability that I shall pick a yellow sweet?
6) When a football team plays a match, the result is either win, lose or draw. Assuming all results to be equally likely, find the probability that
   (a) a single match will be a draw
   (b) a single match will not be a draw
   (c) two matches will both result in a draw
   (d) three matches will all result in a draw
7) (a) Three coins are tossed together. Copy and complete this table to find all the different ways (the sample space) the coins can land (H=heads, T=tails)

COIN 1	H	H		
COIN 2	H	H		
COIN 3	H	T		etc.

   (b) From your answer to (a) find
      (i) the probability of all three coins landing tails up
      (ii) the probability of the coins landing with one head and two tails
   (c) Without listing all the possibilities, try to work out the probability of four coins all landing heads up when they are tossed together.

A MEAN, MODE, MEDIAN & RANGE

Mean

The correct name is 'arithmetic mean'. Mean is often called 'average'. The mean is calculated by adding together all the quantities (or amounts) and dividing the total by how many quantities (or amounts) there are, e.g. in this group of 30 numbers

3 9 7 0 7 1 5 2 3 8 6 4 5 8 6
0 4 9 7 1 3 6 2 1 8 5 0 4 8 3

the total of the numbers is 135, so the mean is

$$\frac{135}{30} = 4\,{}^{1}\!/_{2}$$

Mode

The mode (or modal value) of a group of quantities is the quantity which occurs, or happens, most often in the group, e.g. in this group

69 72 75 68 62 70 63 68 66
71 68 64 73 70 69 59 67 71

the mode is 68 because it occurs more often than any other number.

Median

If a group of quantities is listed in order of size, the median is the middle quantity in the list, e.g. to find the median of

17 22 23 16 24 20 16 23 19 21 26

arrange in order of size

16 16 17 19 20 21 22 23 23 24 26

The median is 21 because it is the middle quantity.

If the group contains an EVEN number of quantities, the median is half–way between the middle quantities (or the mean of the two middle quantities), e.g. to find the median of

42 48 41 44 47 49 ,

arrange in order of size 41 42 44 47 48 49

The median is $45\frac{1}{2}$ (half–way between 44 and 47, or the mean of 44 and 47).

D Range

The range of a group of quantities is found by subtracting the smallest quantity from the largest, e.g.

in the group 83 82 87 84 92 88 78 80

the range is 92 − 78 = 14

a

Find the mean of each group of numbers

1) 53, 55, 49, 57, 63, 52, 59, 60
2) 20, 18, 26, 32, 15, 42, 25, 16, 28, 19, 23
3) 4, 12, 7, 8, 6, 2, 5, 11, 5, 16, 6, 9, 7, 10, 8, 4
4) 35, 27, 35, 47, 29, 40, 37, 36, 38
5) 6, 4, 3, 7, 8, 5, 3, 7, 2, 3, 3, 8, 9, 4, 1, 5, 6, 6, 3, 2

---

b

Find the mode of each group

1) 7, 5, 3, 6, 1, 8, 6, 7, 3, 9, 4, 5, 6, 2, 9, 4
2) 8, 5, 6, 5, 7, 8, 5, 4, 7, 5, 6, 8, 5, 6
3) 72, 75, 71, 73, 68, 69, 79, 73, 71, 71, 74, 69, 73, 67, 73, 76
4) B, A, S, E, B, A, L, L, M, A, T, C, H, E, S
5) 44, 43, 41, 47, 45, 43, 47, 41, 47
   44, 46, 41, 44, 47, 48, 42, 40, 43

---

c

Find the median of each group of numbers

1) 42, 48, 54, 43, 56, 52, 41, 47, 48, 52, 49, 45, 50
2) 4, 2, 3, 6, 8, 5, 7, 9, 2, 5, 4, 1, 3, 7, 8, 4, 1
3) 123, 118, 127, 133, 128, 122, 128, 119, 130, 121
4) 18, 15, 16, 25, 13, 19, 30, 22, 27, 16, 33, 22, 17, 24, 14
5) 77, 82, 78, 77, 79, 82, 78, 80, 77
   79, 83, 81, 82, 78, 77, 81, 80, 81

---

d

For each of these groups of numbers, work out
(a) the mean, (b) the mode, (c) the median, (d) the range

1)

5	7	8	7	4	6	1	2	4	7
4	9	4	6	1	8	2	6	8	1

2)

24	28	23	24	34	27	24	26	24	29
25	21	28	30	25	27	29	19	28	27
25	27	24	32	20					

3)

94	72	58	85	61	54	80	56	74	66

4)

12	17	16	20	14	9	22	15	16	20
17	12	21	19	16	10	15	12	21	11
16	20	10	24	9	21	8	16	23	18

5)

6	10	4	12	7	5	12	3	11	3	15	8
9	2	10	9	4	11	6	12	16	5	9	13
3	1	9	11	8	2	7	19	10	4	14	7

A TRIGONOMETRY (1)

Trigonometry means 'measuring three–cornered figures'. It shows the connection (or relationship) between the angles and the sides of a triangle.
This book shows only the simplest kind of trigonometry using SINE (sin), COSINE (cos), and TANGENT (tan).

Right-angled triangle

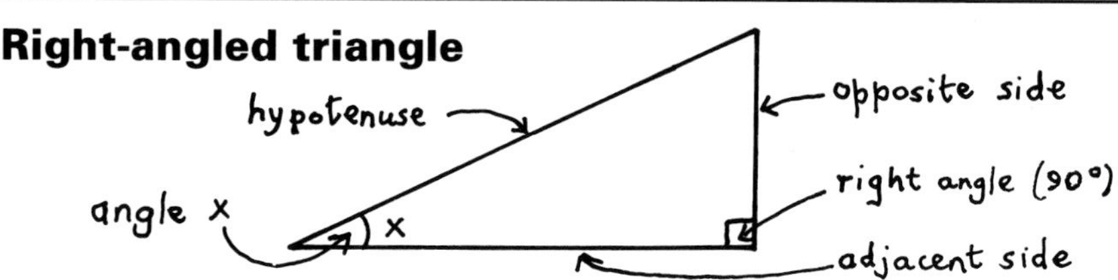

The longest side of a right-angled triangle is the HYPOTENUSE (H).
The shorter side next to the angle x is the ADJACENT SIDE (A).
The side opposite the angle x is the OPPOSITE SIDE (O).

SINE of an angle = opposite side ÷ hypotenuse ($S = \frac{O}{H}$)

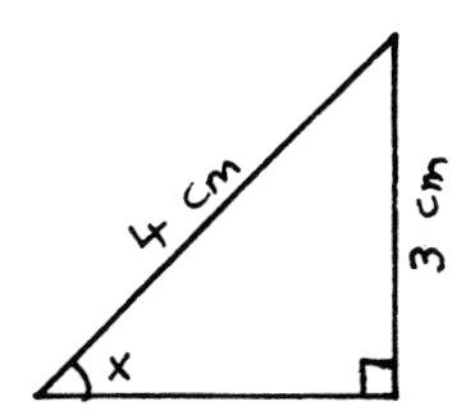

e.g. $\sin x = \frac{\text{opposite}}{\text{hypotenuse}} = \frac{3}{4} = 0.75$ (2dp)

The size of angle x, to the nearest degree, can be found on page 72 by looking for 0.75 in the sin column and reading the angle size on the left

Angle x = 49°

(*on a calculator* [•] [7] [5] [INV] [SIN])

COSINE of an angle = adjacent side ÷ hypotenuse ($C = \frac{A}{H}$)

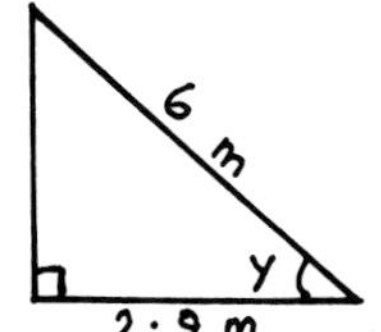

e.g. $\cos y = \frac{\text{adjacent}}{\text{hypotenuse}} = \frac{2.9}{6} = 0.48$ (2dp)

From the cos column on page 72

Angle y = 61°

(*on a calculator* [•] [4] [8] [INV] [COS])

TANGENT of an angle = opposite side ÷ adjacent side ($T = \frac{O}{A}$)

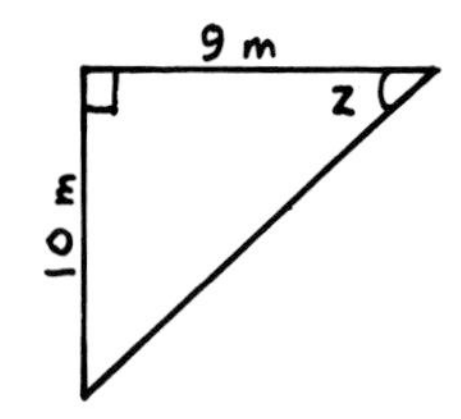

e.g. $\tan z = \frac{\text{opposite}}{\text{adjacent}} = \frac{10}{9} = 1.11$ (2 dp)

From the tan column on page 72

Angle z = 48°

(*on a calculator* [1] [•] [1] [1] [INV] [TAN])

a (Triangles on this page are not drawn to scale)

Work out the sines of angles a, b, c, d, e correct to 2 decimal places. Then, by looking in the sin column on page 72, write down, to the nearest degree, the size of each angle.

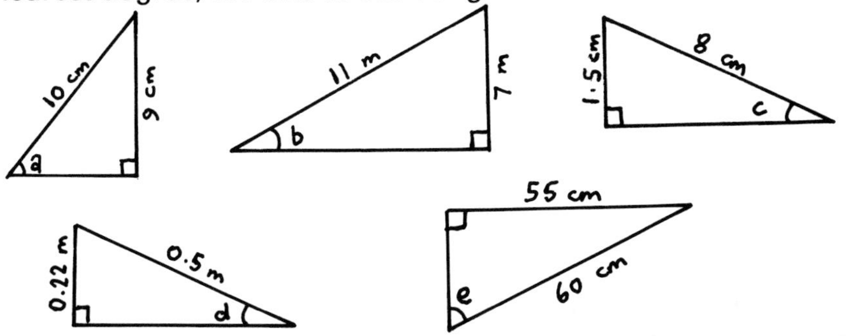

b Work out the cosines of angles f, g, h, j, k correct to 2 decimal places. Then, by looking in the cos column on page 72, write down, to the nearest degree, the size of each angle.

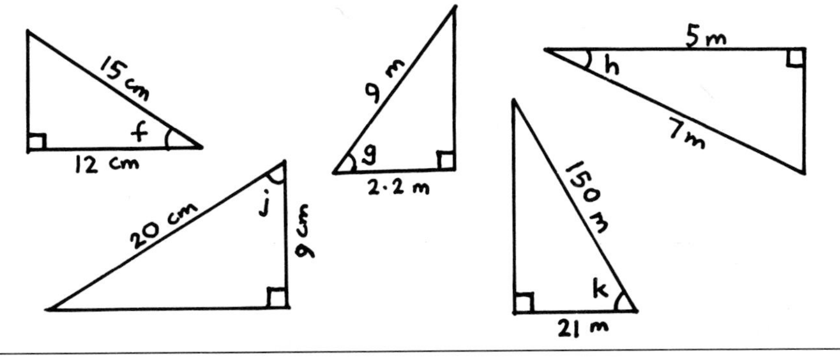

c Work out the tangents of angles l, m, n, p, q correct to 2 decimal places. Then, by looking in the tan column on page 72, write down, to the nearest degree, the size of each angle.

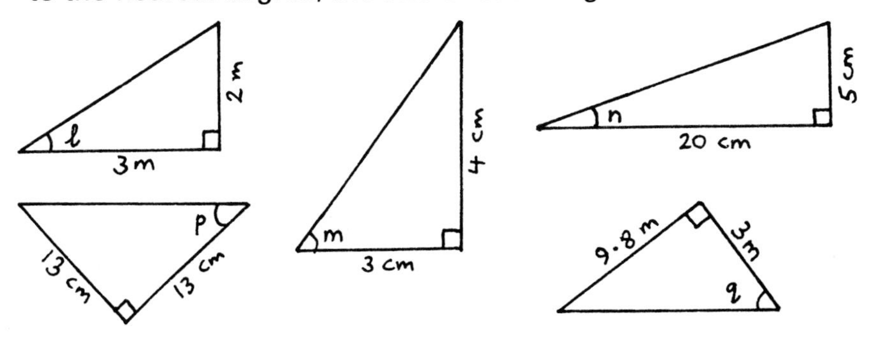

A TRIGONOMETRY (2)

Sine (sin)

$$\sin x = \frac{\text{opposite}}{\text{hypotenuse}}$$

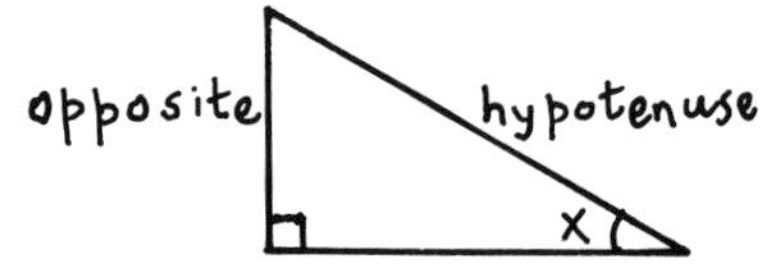

e.g. (1) Find the length y, correct to 2 significant figures

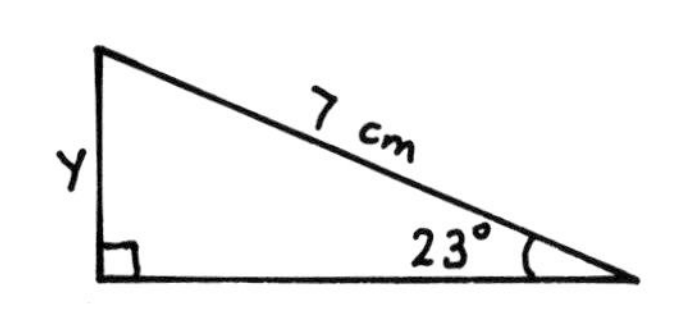

$\sin 23° = \frac{y}{7}$

$y = 7 \sin 23°$

$= 7 \times 0.39$

$= 2.7$ cm (2 sig. figs.)

(*on a calculator* [2] [3] [SIN] [X] [7])

---

e.g. (2) Find the length c

$\sin 30° = \frac{6}{c}$

$c = \frac{6}{\sin 30°}$

$= \frac{6}{0.50}$

$= 12$ cm (2 sig. figs)

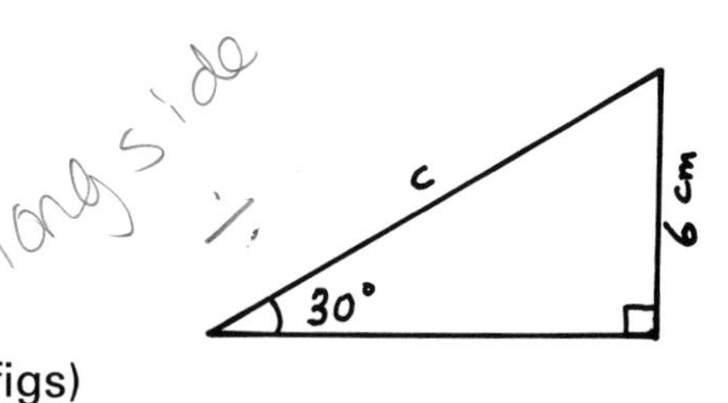

---

e.g. (3) A straight pine tree 17 metres tall is blown over in a gale so that its top rests against a vertical building.

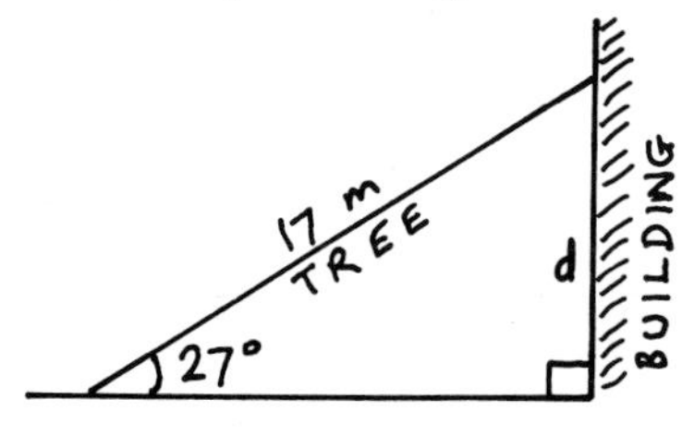

The ground between the foot of the tree and the base of the building is level, and the tree makes an angle of 27° with the ground. How far up the building (d) is the top of the tree?

$\sin 27° = \frac{d}{17}$

$d = 17 \sin 27°$

$= 17 \times 0.45 = 7.7$ (2 sig. figs)

The top of the tree is 7.7 metres up the building

REMEMBER the short way of writing expressions in trigonometry, e.g. 3 sin 47° is short for 3 X the sine of 47°.

USE THE TABLE ON PAGE 72 OR AN ELECTRONIC CALCULATOR. GIVE ANSWERS CORRECT TO 2 SIGNIFICANT FIGURES.

a Write down the value of each of these. Remember that, for example, '6 sin 51°' means '6 X the sine of 51°'.

1) sin 37°
2) sin 84°
3) sin 11°
4) sin 76°
5) sin 4°
6) sin 55°
7) sin 17°
8) 3 sin 27°
9) 5 sin 40°
10) 2 sin 59°

b Find the lengths a, b, c, d and e in these diagrams (not drawn to scale)

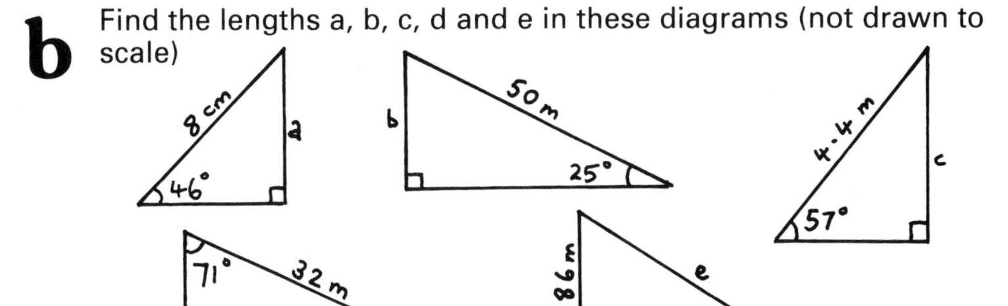

c Use sines to work these out. Make a rough drawing each time.

1) The top of a sloping plank 2.5m long just touches the top of a vertical wall. The bottom of the plank and the bottom of the wall are on level ground and the plank makes an angle of 37° with the ground. Find the height of the wall.

2) Maldon (M) is due east of Chelmsford (C). Basildon (B) is due south of Chelmsford. The distance from Basildon to Maldon is 23km and $C\hat{B}M = 40°$. How far is Maldon from Chelmsford?

3) The jib of a crane is 30m long and makes an angle of 43° with the ground. Calculate the vertical height of the top of the jib.

4) The diagram shows a steep road (ST) climbing a hill from the sea shore (S). If a car is at point T, how far above sea level is it (RT)?

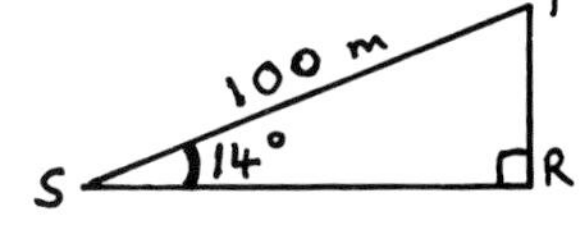

5) An aircraft attempting to fly due north is blown off course so that it follows a bearing 012°. After flying 15 km, how much further east is it than it should be?

A TRIGONOMETRY (3)

Cosine (cos)

$$\cos x = \frac{\text{adjacent}}{\text{hypotenuse}}$$

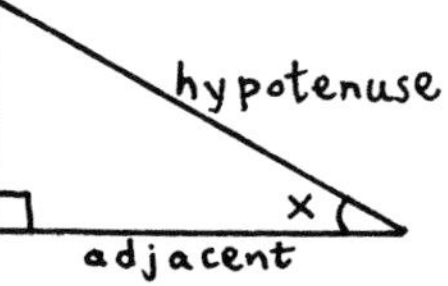

e.g. (1) Find the length of d (to 2 significant figures)

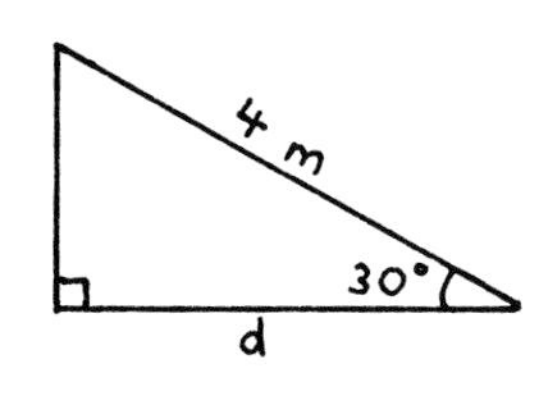

$$\cos 30° = \frac{d}{4}$$

d = 4 cos 30°
= 4 X 0.87
= 3.5m (2 sig. figs)
(*on a calculator* [3][0] [COS] [X] [4])

---

e.g. (2) Find the length of AC, correct to 2 significant figures

$$\cos 57° = \frac{16}{AC}$$

$$AC = \frac{16}{\cos 57}$$

$$= \frac{16}{0.54} = 30\text{m (2 s.f.)}$$

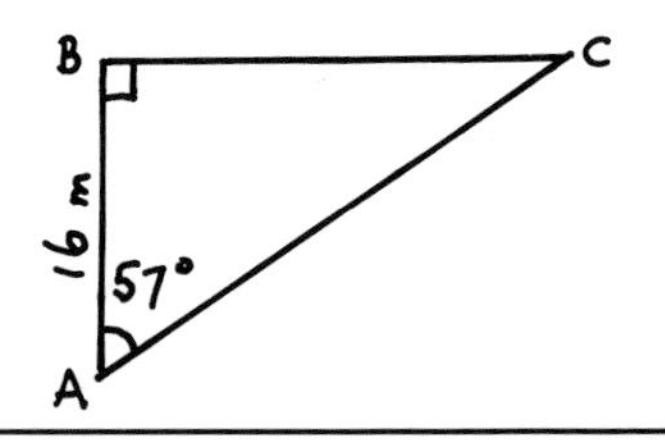

---

e.g. (3) An aeroplane sets off from a landing strip (L) and flies on a bearing 130°. After it has flown 11.5km it drops supplies at a village (V). Then it changes course, heading due north on another mission, and passes over a farmstead (F) which is due east of the landing strip. How far, correct to 2 significant figures, is the farmstead from the landing strip?

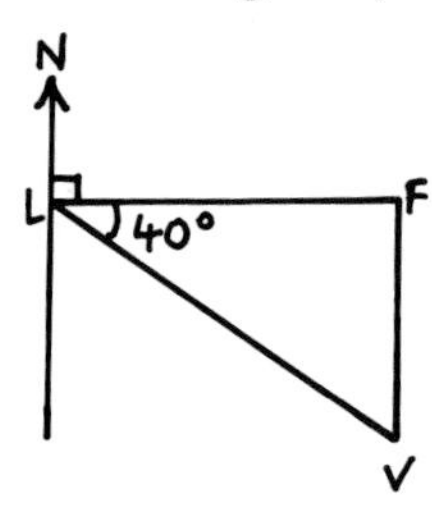

The aeroplane is flying on a bearing 130°, so angle FLV = 130–90 = 40°

$$\cos 40° = \frac{LF}{11.5}$$

LF = 11.5 cos 40°
= 11.5 x 0.77 = 8.9

The farmstead is 8.9km from the landing strip (2 sig. figs.)

NOTE. The cosine of x° has the same value as the sine of (90 – x)°,

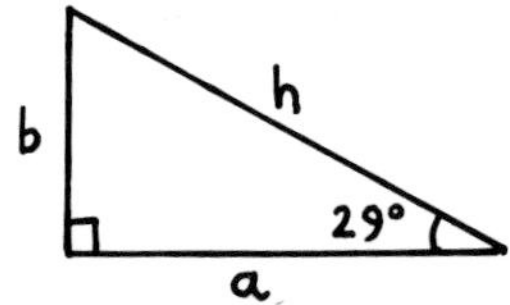

e.g.
cos 29° = sin 61° = a/h
sin 29° = cos 61° = b/h

USE THE TABLE ON PAGE 72 OR AN ELECTRONIC CALCULATOR. GIVE ANSWERS CORRECT TO 2 SIGNIFICANT FIGURES.

a

Write down the value of each of these

1) cos 53°
2) cos 17°
3) cos 84°
4) cos 41°
5) cos 77°
6) cos 63°
7) 4 cos 82°
8) 2 cos 59°
9) 7 cos 70°
10) 3 cos 34°

b

Find the lengths f, g, h, j and k in these diagrams (not drawn to scale)

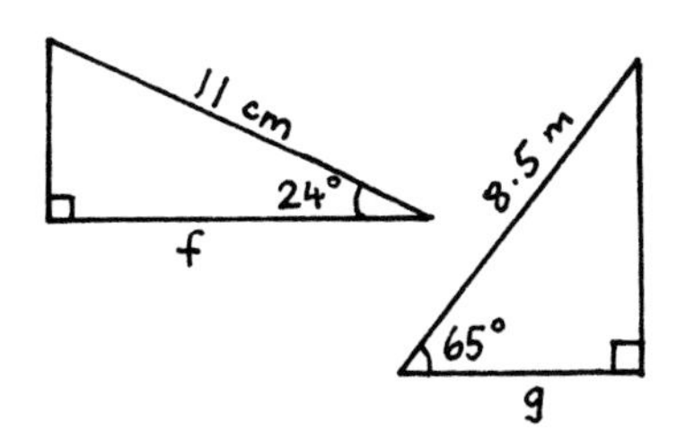

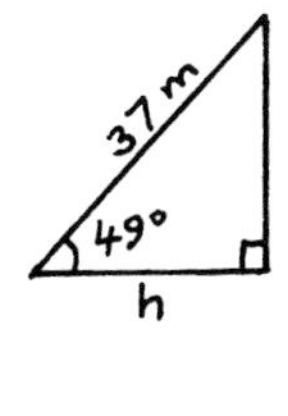

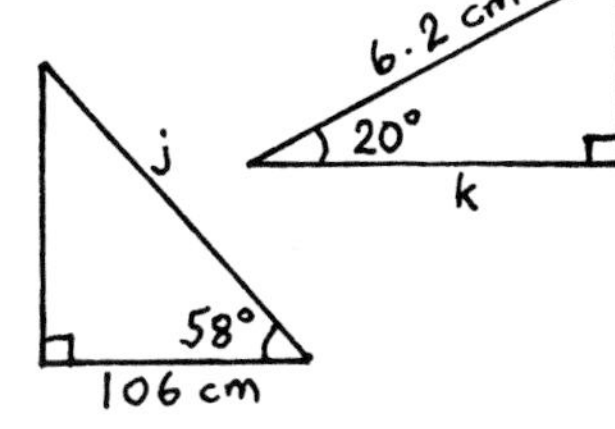

c

Use cosines to work these out. Make a rough drawing each time.

1) A ladder is propped against a vertical wall with its foot on level ground 2.7m from the wall. The ladder makes an angle of 69° with the ground. How long is the ladder?

2)

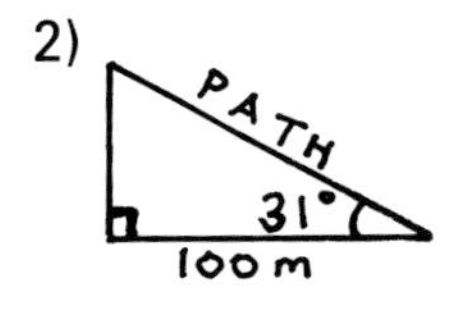

The distance from the bottom to the top of Howden Hill is shown on a map as 100m. The hill makes an angle of 31° with the level ground. How long is the path which goes from the bottom to the top of the hill?

3) From a harbour, a boat sails 6km on a bearing 145°, then changes course and sails due west until it is due south of the harbour. How far must it now sail to return to the harbour?

4) A straight road runs due west to due east. Thomas and Stephen set off from a point 2.4km due south of the road. Thomas walks due north; Stephen walks on a bearing 041°. How much further than Thomas does Stephen walk before reaching the road?

5) A piece of play apparatus consists of a flight of steps AD, 3m long, at an angle of 62° to the ground, connected at D to a slide DC, 5m long, at an angle of 32° to the ground. By calculating the lengths of AB and BC, work out the distance between the bottom of the steps and the bottom of the slide.

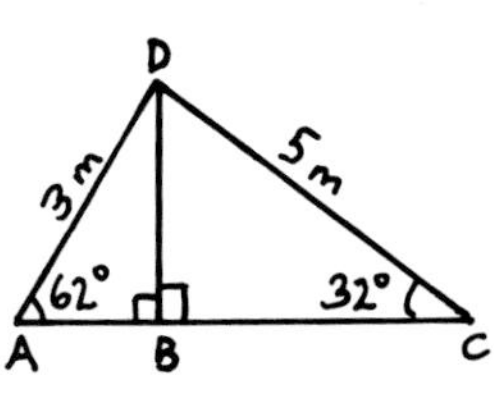

A TRIGONOMETRY (4)

Tangent (tan)

$$\tan x = \frac{\text{opposite}}{\text{adjacent}}$$

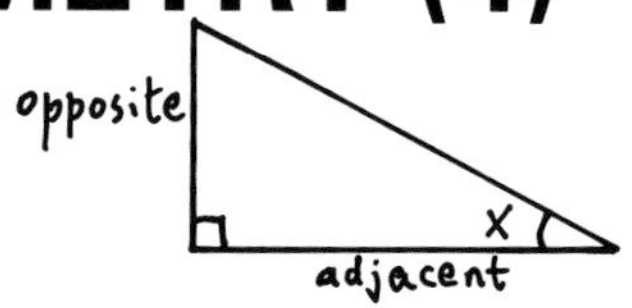

e.g. (1) Find the length of k (to 2 significant figures)

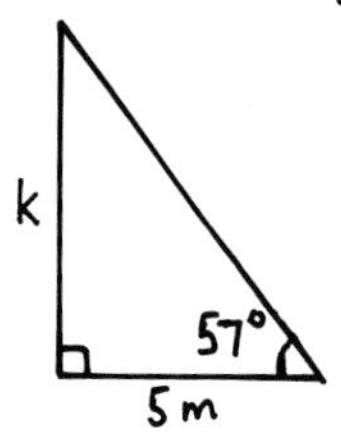

$\tan 57° = \frac{k}{5}$

$k = 5 \tan 57°$
$= 5 \times 1.54$
$= 7.7$m (2 sig. figs)

(*on a calculator* [5] [7] [TAN] [X] [5])

---

e.g. (2) Find the length of PQ, correct to 2 significant figures

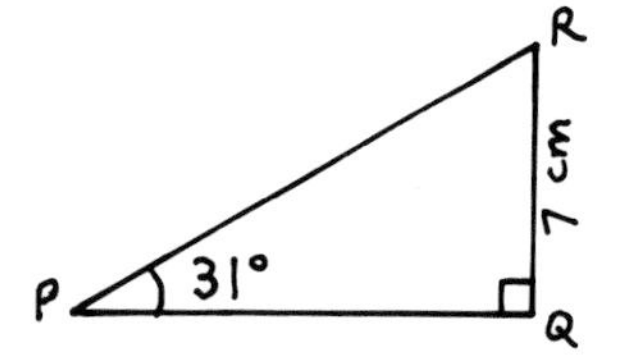

$\tan 31° = \frac{7}{PQ}$

$PQ = \frac{7}{\tan 31°} = \frac{7}{0.60} = 12$cm (2 sig. figs)

Another way

$P\hat{R}Q = 59°$ (angles in a triangle = 180°)

$\tan 59° = \frac{PQ}{7}$, so $PQ = 7 \tan 59° = 7 \times 1.66 = 12$cm (2sf)

B

Measuring heights with a clinometer

e.g. A girl stands on level ground exactly 15 metres from the foot of a vertical flagpole. She points a clinometer at the top of the flagpole and reads off an angle of 28°. What is the height (H) of the flagpole?

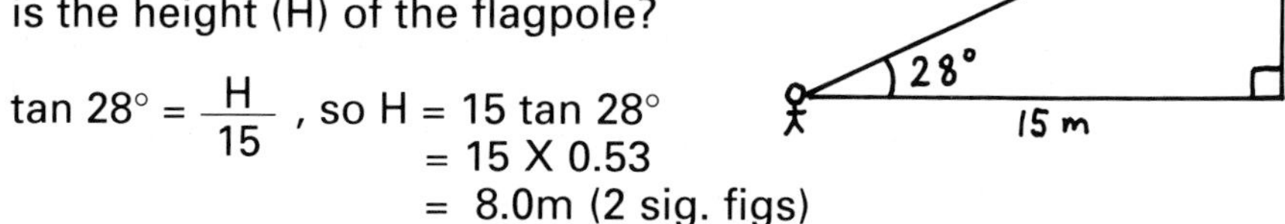

$\tan 28° = \frac{H}{15}$, so $H = 15 \tan 28°$
$= 15 \times 0.53$
$= 8.0$m (2 sig. figs)

NOTE If the girl's eye is (e.g.) 1.3m above the ground when she uses the clinometer, an extra 1.3m must be added to the answer to find the correct height of the flagpole (from the ground to the top). The flagpole in this example is really 8.0 + 1.3 = 9.3 metres high (2 sig. figs)

USE THE TABLE ON PAGE 72 OR AN ELECTRONIC CALCULATOR. GIVE ANSWERS CORRECT TO 2 SIGNIFICANT FIGURES.

a

Write down the value of each of these

1) tan 7°
2) tan 61°
3) tan 37°
4) tan 79°
5) tan 45°
6) 4 tan 63°
7) 2 tan 19°
8) tan 26°
9) 5 tan 44°
10) 9 tan 21°

b

Find the lengths n, p, q, r and s in these diagrams (not drawn to scale)

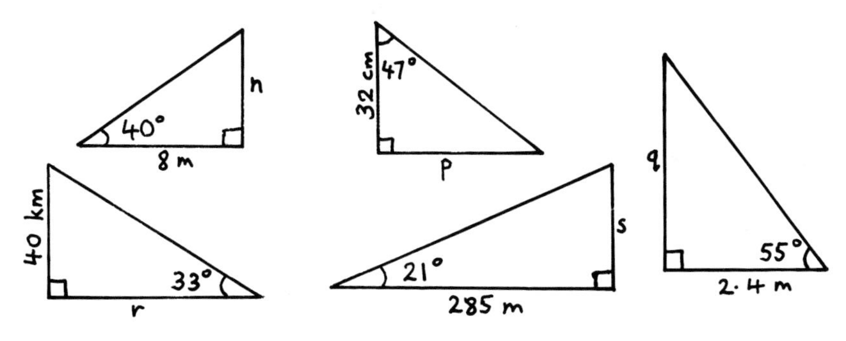

c

Use tangents to work these out. Make a rough drawing each time.

1) A boy stands on level ground 200m from the foot of a tower and observes the top of the tower with a clinometer which shows an angle of 19°. Find the height of the tower.

2) William walks 500m due east (090°) from a pine tree (T) and stops. David walks from T on a bearing 060° until he is due north of William. How far is David from William?

3) The base (AB) of a rectangular window ABCD is 44cm long. The diagonal AC makes an angle of 60° with the base. How high is the window?

4) A helicopter is directly above a lighthouse and is hovering at 315m above sea level. An observer on a yacht points a clinometer at the helicopter and records an angle of 12°. Calculate the distance of the yacht from the lighthouse.

5) A man uses a clinometer to measure the height of a tree. He stands 20m from the tree on level ground and points the clinometer at the top of the tree. The clinometer records an angle of 25°. (a) What is the height of the tree from the man's eye? (b) If the man's eye is 1.6m above the ground, what is the correct height of the tree?

A TRIGONOMETRY (5)

Calculations using sine, cosine or tangent

$\text{SINE} = \frac{\text{OPPOSITE}}{\text{HYPOTENUSE}}$ | $\text{COSINE} = \frac{\text{ADJACENT}}{\text{HYPOTENUSE}}$ | $\text{TANGENT} = \frac{\text{OPPOSITE}}{\text{ADJACENT}}$

To find out which formula to use, see which sides of the triangle you either **know** or are **trying to find**, e.g. Find the length of PQ

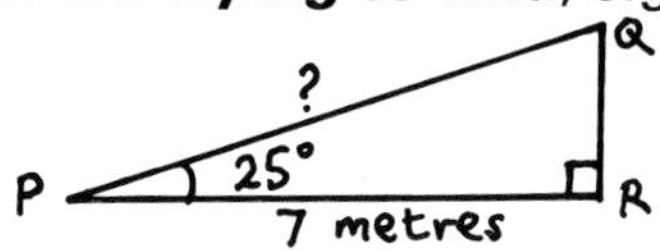

In this triangle, we **know** the length PR (ADJACENT side) and we are **trying to find** the length PQ (HYPOTENUSE), so we use the COSINE formula

$$\cos 25° = \frac{7}{PQ} \textbf{ or } PQ = \frac{7}{\cos 25°} = 7.7\text{m (1 dp)}$$

(The length QR is of no interest to us in this calculation.)

e.g. (2) Find the length d

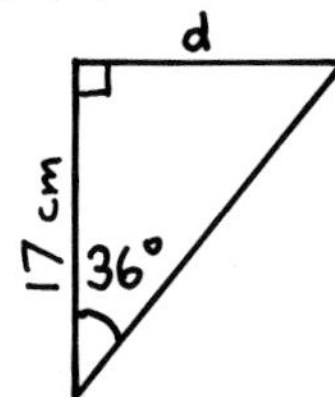

In this triangle we **know** the ADJACENT side which is 17 cm long, and we are **trying to find** the OPPOSITE side (d).

We use the TANGENT formula

$$\tan 36° = \frac{d}{17} \textbf{ or } d = 17 \tan 36° = 12.4\text{cm (1dp)}$$

B Angle of elevation; angle of depression

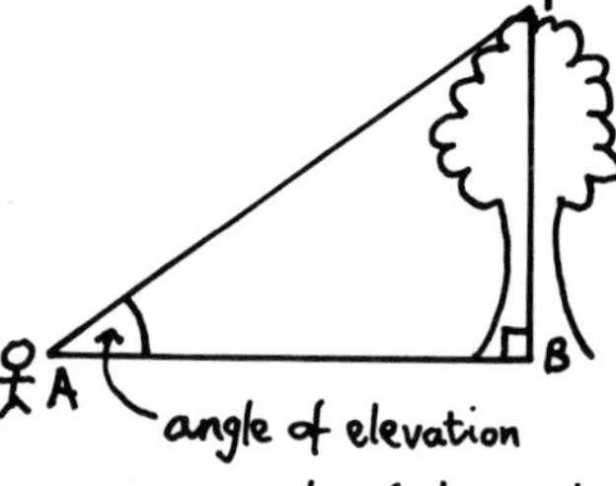

Angle of elevation is the angle which a point makes above the horizontal

e.g. $T\hat{A}B$ is the angle of elevation of the tree top (T) from the person (A) looking at it.

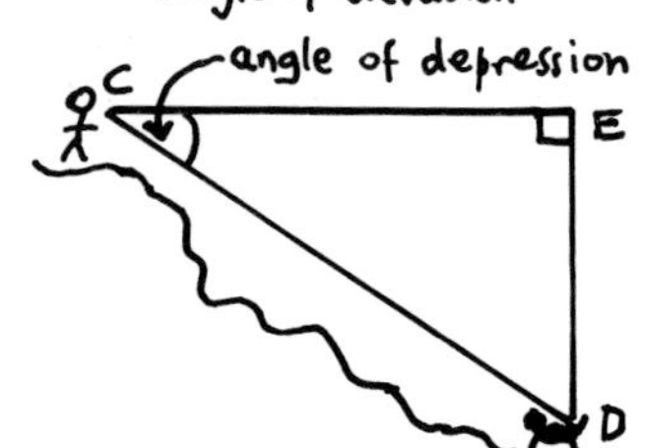

Angle of depression is the angle which a point makes below the horizontal

e.g. $E\hat{C}D$ is the angle of depression of the dog (D) from the person (C) looking at it.

USE THE TABLE ON PAGE 72 OR AN ELECTRONIC CALCULATOR. GIVE ANSWERS CORRECT TO 2 SIGNIFICANT FIGURES.

a

Find the lengths a, b, c, d, e, f, g, h, j, k.

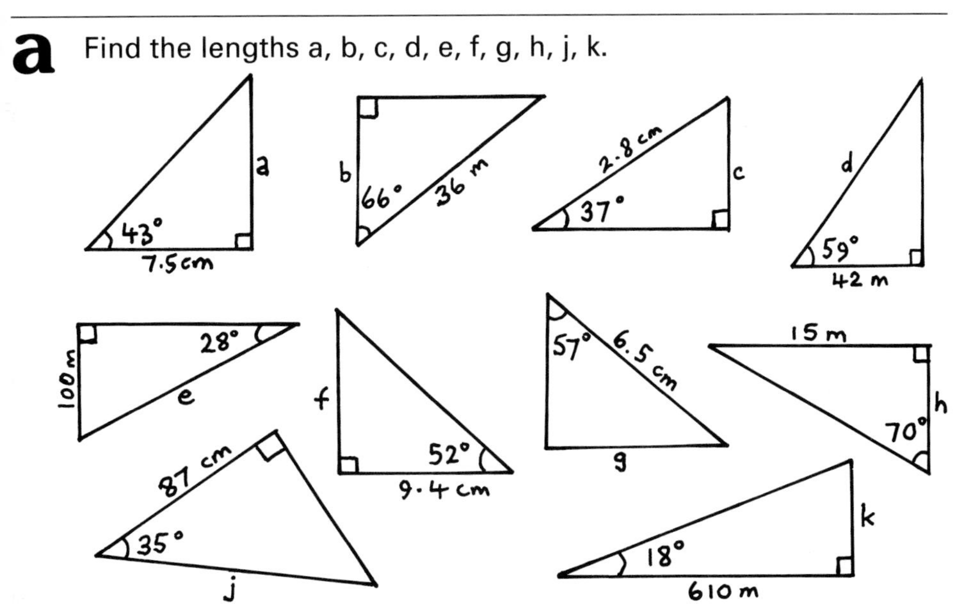

b

1) A boat on a horizontal sea is 90m from the top of a vertical cliff. The angle of elevation of the cliff top from the boat is 20°. How high above sea level is the cliff top?

2) A fisherman (F) and a bird watcher (B) sit 40m apart on the same bank of a straight river. A willow tree (W) grows on the other bank exactly opposite the bird watcher. Angle $B\hat{F}W$ is 32°. Calculate (a) the width of the river; (b) the distance between the fisherman and the willow tree.

3) 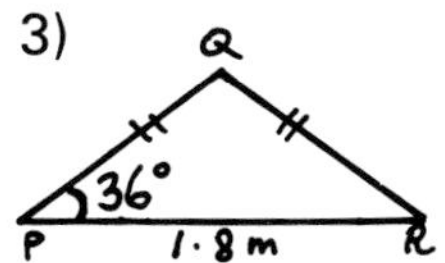

The diagram shows the cross section of the roof of a shed. The owner of the shed wishes to cover the sloping part with roofing felt. What length (PQR) of felt will be needed?

4) Amy looks out of an upstairs window of her house and observes Kate who is standing outside on level ground 10.5m from the house. The angle of depression of Kate from Amy is 24°. Find Amy's height above the ground.

5) The villages of Cantwell and Meakin Brow, which are 1.5km apart, are respectively at the bottom and top of a steady slope which makes an angle of 8° with the horizontal. Calculate, in metres, the difference in height above sea level of the two villages.

A CIRCLE (1)

Centre of a circle is the point in the exact middle of the circle. It is nearly always given the letter O.

Radius of a circle is a straight line from the centre to the perimeter (circumference) of the circle. It is usually called r or R.

Diameter of a circle is a straight line which passes through the centre and crosses the circle from side to side. It is usually called d or D.

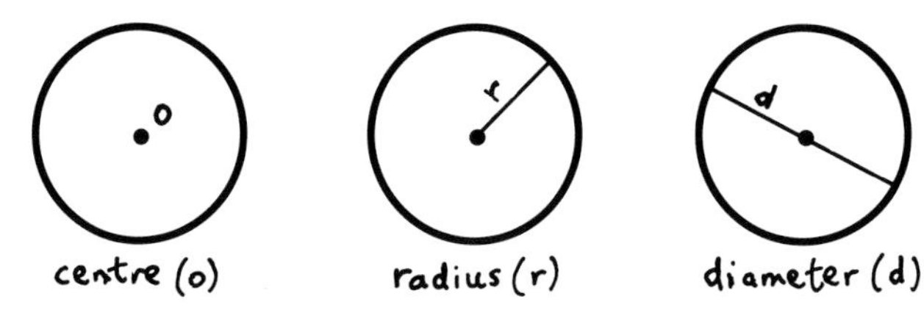

The diameter is twice the length of the radius $d = 2r$

π is a Greek letter 'pi' (pronounced like apple **pie**) which stands for a number. π is a complicated decimal which goes on for ever but does not recur. It is roughly equal to 3.14 or $\frac{22}{7}$ and is used for many circle calculations

---

Circumference (C) is the perimeter of a circle (all the way round the outside)

Circumference = π X diameter
or Circumference = 2 X π X radius

$$C = 2\pi r$$

e.g. (1) ($\pi = 3.14$) Find the circumference of a circle whose radius is 5cm.

$C = 2 \times 3.14 \times 5$
$= 31.4$ Circumference is 31.4cm

e.g. (2) ($\pi = \frac{22}{7}$) Calculate the circumference of a circle with radius 28cm.

$C = 2 \times \frac{22}{7} \times 28$

$= 176$ Circumference is 176 cm

a Find the diameter of a circle whose radius is

1) 3cm
2) 4.7cm
3) 62cm
4) 25mm
5) 94m

---

b Find the radius of a circle whose diameter is

1) 82m
2) 34cm
3) 14.6cm
4) 11 miles
5) 7.5 cm

---

c ($\pi = 3.14$) Calculate, correct to 2 significant figures, the circumference of a circle whose radius is

1) 1km
2) 9cm
3) 0.5m
4) 4cm
5) 2.4m
6) 3cm
7) 12cm
8) 6.5m
9) 15cm
10) 0.8m

---

d ($\pi = \frac{22}{7}$) Calculate the circumference of a circle whose radius is

1) 7cm
2) 350m
3) 21cm
4) $\frac{1}{11}$ m
5) $1\frac{2}{5}$ m
6) 77cm
7) 56m
8) x cm
9) $6\frac{3}{10}$ cm
10) $10\frac{1}{2}$ m

---

e ($\pi = 3.14$) Give answers to 2 significant figures

1) Find the perimeter of a semicircle whose radius is 4cm

2) A bicycle has a wheel with radius 30cm. By finding the circumference of the wheel, calculate how far the bicycle travels when the wheel turns round 5 times.

3) The minute hand of a large clock is 4m long.
What distance does the tip of the hand travel in

(a) 1 hour?

(b) 20 minutes?

4) Find the circumference of a car steering wheel which has a diameter of 38cm

5)

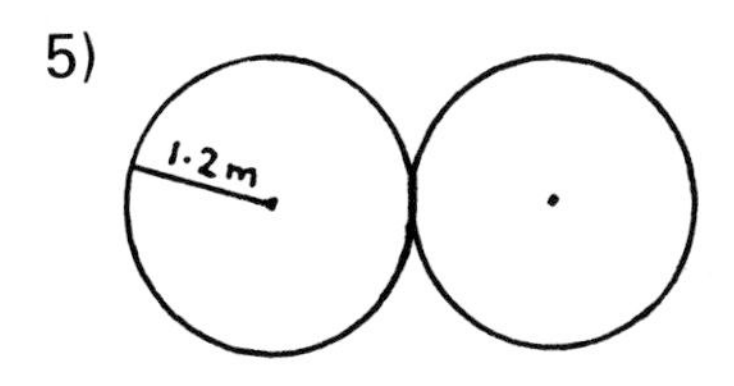

A simple model railway track is in the shape of a figure eight made out of two circles each of radius 1.2m. Calculate the complete length of the track.

A CIRCLE (2)

Area (A) of a circle

Area = π X radius X radius

$A = \pi r^2$

e.g. ($\pi = 3.14$) Find the area of a circle whose radius is 15cm

$A = 3.14 \times 15 \times 15$

$A = 706.5$ Area is 706.5 cm^2

e.g. (2) ($\pi = \frac{22}{7}$) Calculate the area of a circle whose radius is 21m

$A = \frac{22}{7} \times \frac{21}{1} \times \frac{21}{1}$

$A = 1386$ Area is 1386m^2

e.g. (3) ($\pi = 3.14$) A semicircle has a radius of 3cm. What is its area, correct to 3 significant figures?

Area of semicircle = $\frac{1}{2}(\pi r^2)$

$A = \frac{1}{2}(3.14 \times 3 \times 3)$

$A = 14.13$ Area is 14.1cm^2 (3 sig. figs.)

B Area of an annulus

An annulus is a ring formed by two concentric circles.

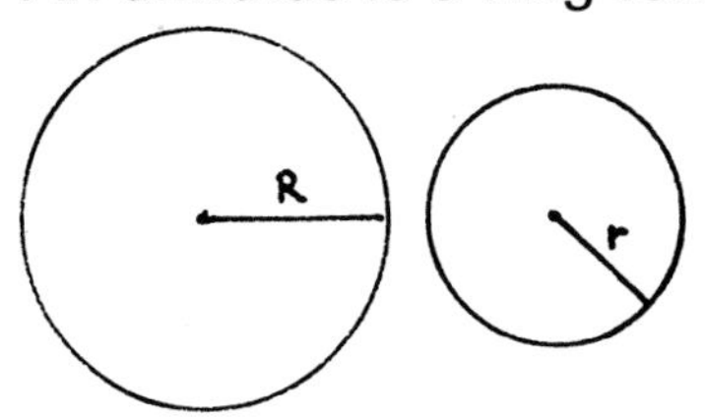

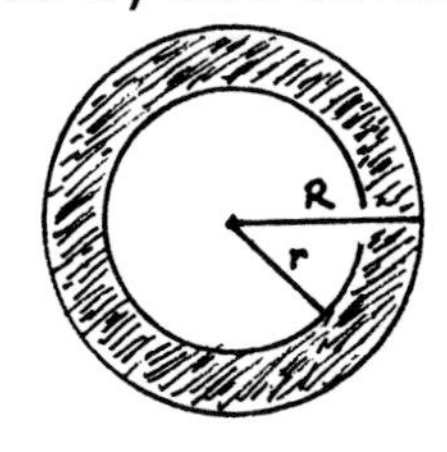

Radius of large circle is R

Radius of small circle is r

Area of annulus =

area of large circle – area of small circle

$A = \pi R^2 - \pi r^2$

or $A = \pi(R^2 - r^2)$

e.g. ($\pi = 3.14$) Find the area between two concentric circles whose radii are 6cm and 4cm

$A = 3.14(6^2 - 4^2)$

$= 3.14(36 - 16)$

$= 3.14 \times 20$

$= 62.8$ Area is 62.8cm^2

NOTE. $(R^2 - r^2)$ is the DIFFERENCE OF TWO SQUARES (see page 36). It could sometimes be easier to factorise first and use

$A = \pi(R + r)(R - r)$

Give answers correct to 2 significant figures, except in part b where exact answers should be given.

a

($\pi = 3.14$) Find the area of a circle whose radius is

1) 2cm
2) 5cm
3) 0.4m
4) 10cm
5) 3m
6) 9cm
7) 8.3cm
8) 55cm
9) k metres
10) 3.2m

b

($\pi = \frac{22}{7}$) Find the area of a circle whose radius is

1) 14cm
2) 35cm
3) 0.7m
4) 2.8m
5) 4cm
6) $\frac{1}{2}$ km
7) 42m
8) 77cm
9) $\frac{7}{11}$cm
10) y cm

c

($\pi = 3.14$) Find the area of a semicircle whose radius is

1) 6cm
2) 1.6m
3) 0.8m
4) 13cm
5) 66m

d

($\pi = 3.14$) Find the area of an annulus with

1) outer radius 5cm , inner radius 3cm
2) outer radius 10cm, inner radius 8cm
3) outer radius 1.5m, inner radius 0.6m
4) outer radius 13cm, inner radius 5cm
5) outer radius 25cm, inner radius 24cm

e

($\pi = 3.14$)

1) Find the area of a circular archery target which has a radius of 40cm.

2) A circular road-roundabout with radius 7m contains a circular flower bed with radius 5m. The rest of the roundabout is covered with grass. Calculate the grass-covered area.

3) The front of a bird nesting box is made of a piece of wood in the shape of a rectangle 19cm high and 13cm wide. A circular hole with radius 1.5cm is cut out. What area of wood remains?

4) 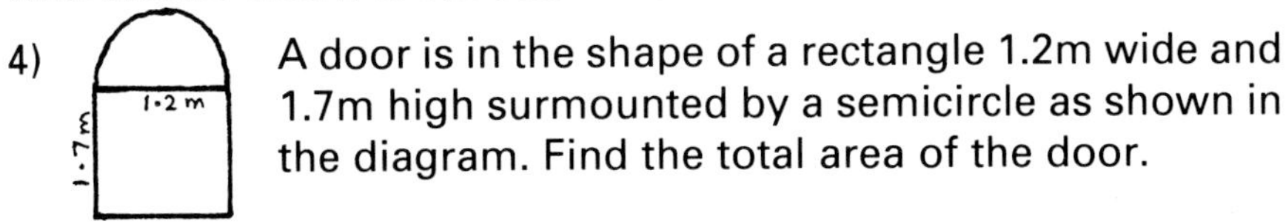

A door is in the shape of a rectangle 1.2m wide and 1.7m high surmounted by a semicircle as shown in the diagram. Find the total area of the door.

5) A circular goldfish pond with radius 3m is surrounded by a stone path 1m wide. Calculate (a) the area of the pond, (b) the area of the path.

A CIRCLE (3)

A **CHORD** is a straight line joining two points on the circumference of a circle.

A **SEGMENT** is one of the regions of a circle formed when the circle is cut by a chord.

An **ARC** is part of the circumference of a circle.

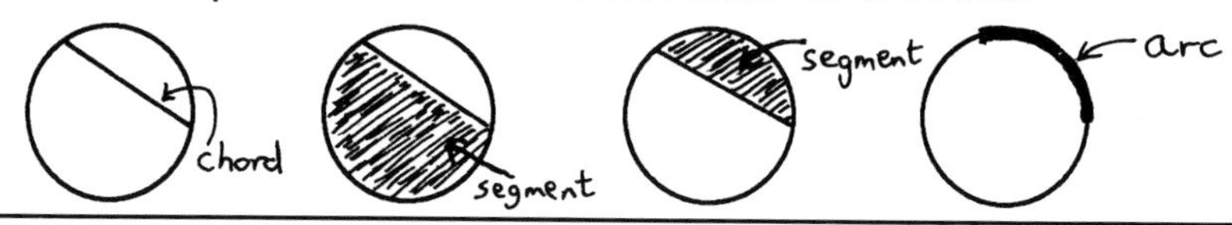

B Angles in the SAME SEGMENT of a circle are EQUAL

e.g.

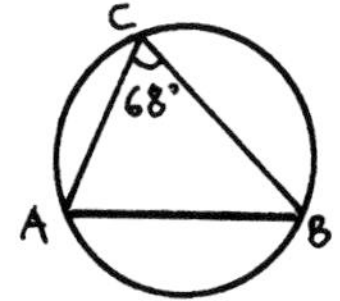

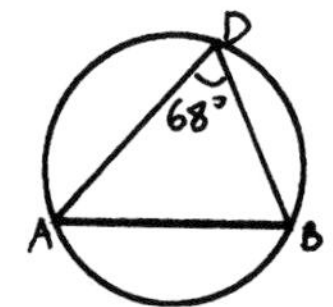

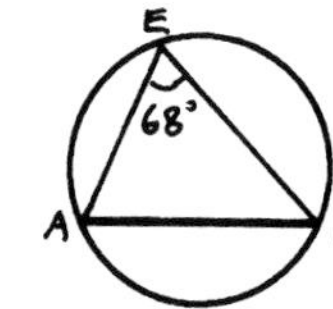

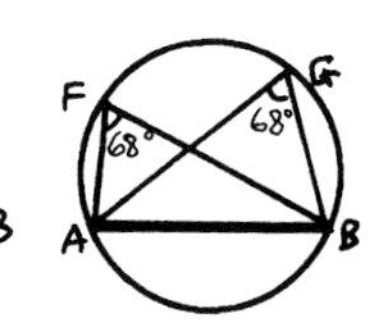

$A\hat{C}B$, $A\hat{D}B$, $A\hat{E}B$, $A\hat{F}B$, and $A\hat{G}B$ are all EQUAL.
They all 'stand' on AB with their 'feet' at A and B. They are all in the same segment of the circle.

C Angles in a SEMICIRCLE are RIGHT ANGLES

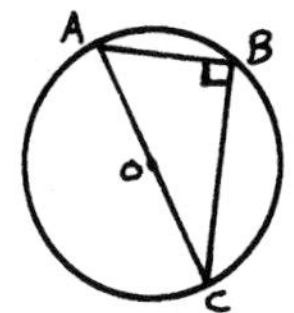

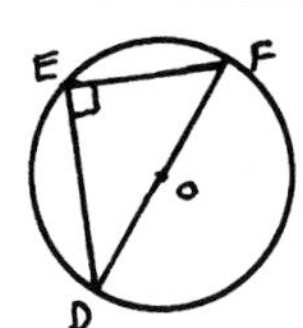

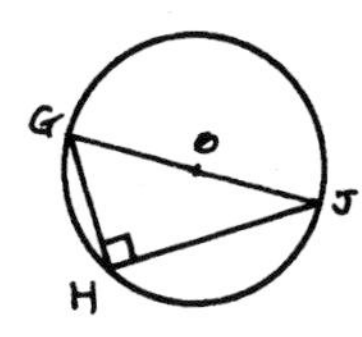

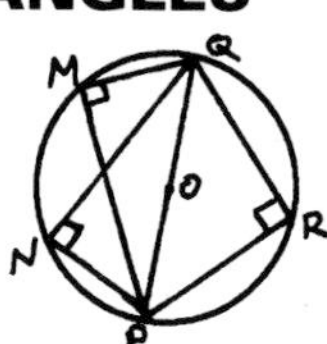

AOC, DOF, GOJ, and POQ are diameters.
$A\hat{B}C$, $D\hat{E}F$, $G\hat{H}J$, $P\hat{M}Q$, $P\hat{N}Q$ and $P\hat{R}Q$ are all right angles (90°).
They are angles in a semicircle.

D Angle at the CENTRE is TWICE the angle at the CIRCUMFERENCE

e.g.

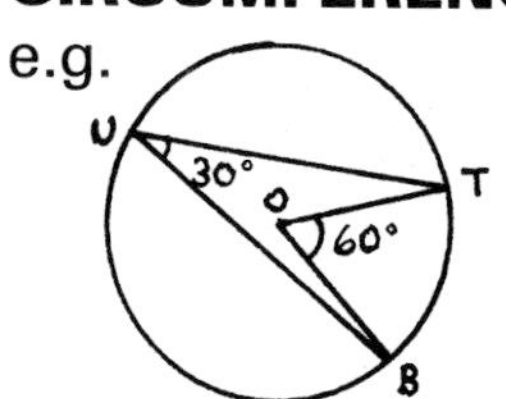

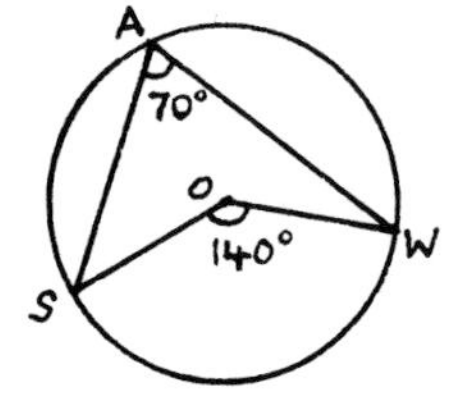

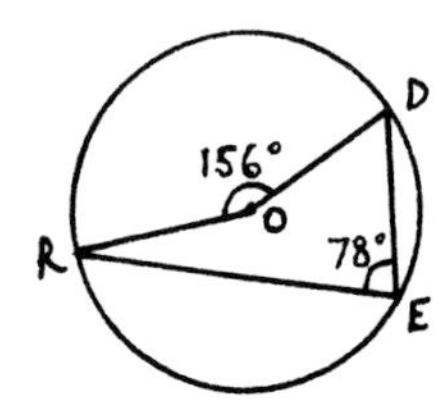

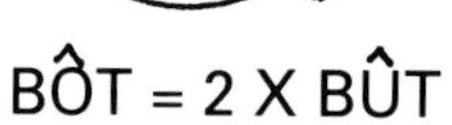

$B\hat{O}T = 2 \times B\hat{U}T$ $S\hat{O}W = 2 \times S\hat{A}W$ $R\hat{O}D = 2 \times R\hat{E}D$

a Find the sizes of angles a, b, c, d, e, (not drawn to scale)

b Find the sizes of angles f, g, h, j and k. O is the centre. POQ, ROS, TOU, VOW and XOY are straight lines.

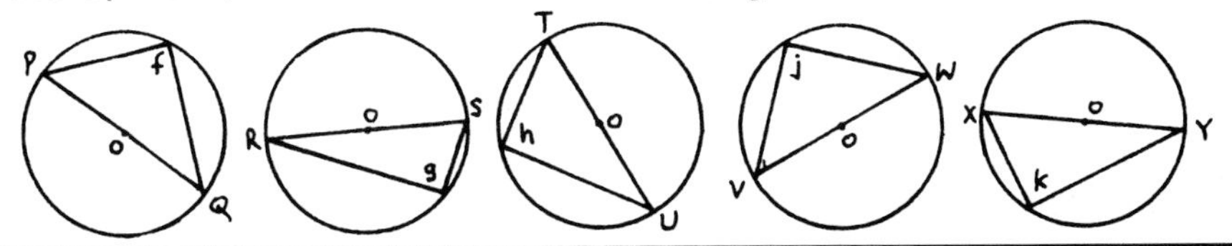

c Find the sizes of angles l, m, n, p, q (not drawn to scale). O is the centre of the circle.

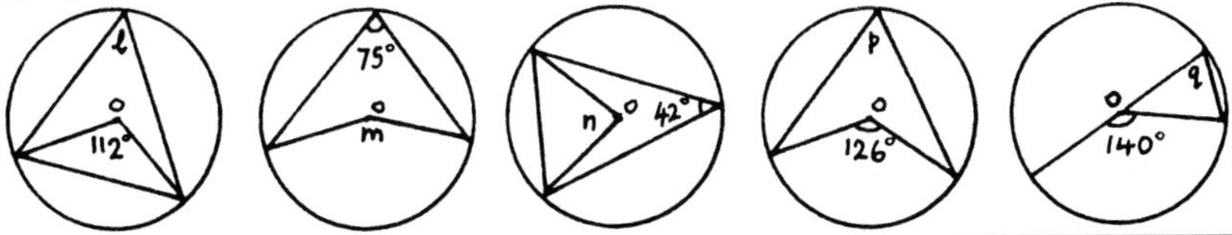

d Find the sizes of angles r, s, t, u, v, w, x, y, z and a (not drawn to scale). O is the centre of the circle.

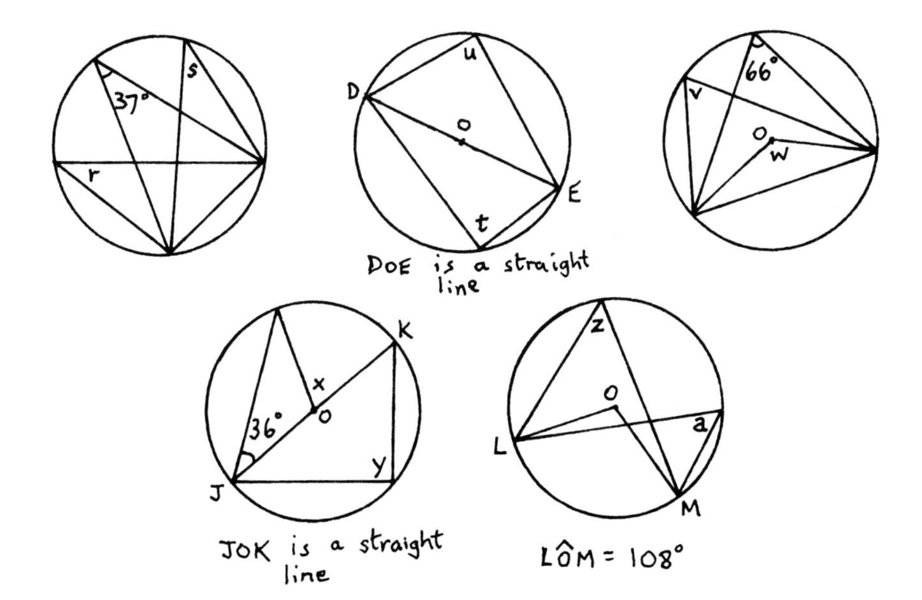

A CIRCLE (4)

Cyclic quadrilateral

A cyclic quadrilateral is a quadrilateral whose four corners touch the circumference of the same circle. A cyclic quadrilateral fits exactly into a circle. The opposite angles of a cyclic quadrilateral add up to 180° (they are supplementary), e.g.

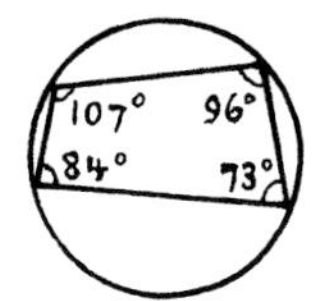

$107° + 73° = 180°$
$96° + 84° = 180°$

e.g. (2) Calculate angles a and b

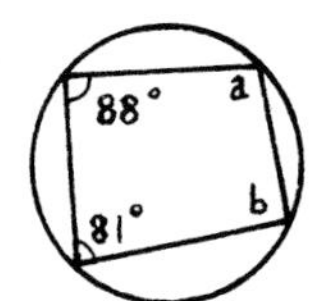

$a = 180° - 81° = 99°$
$b = 180° - 88° = 92°$

B Tangent

A tangent is a straight line, outside a circle, which just touches the circle. At the point where the tangent touches the circle, the tangent is at right angles (90°) to the radius.

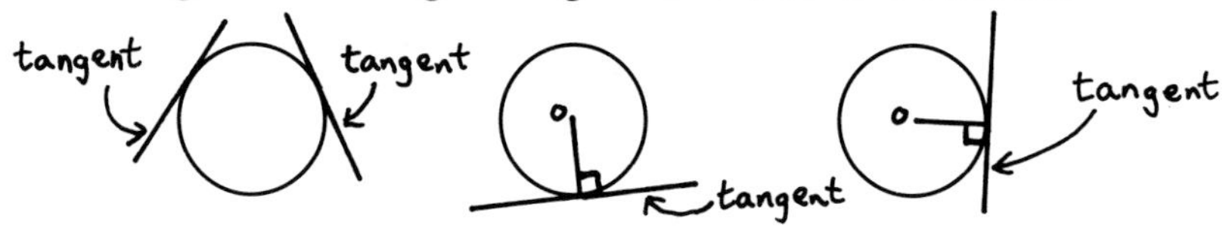

This and other rules provide useful information

e.g.

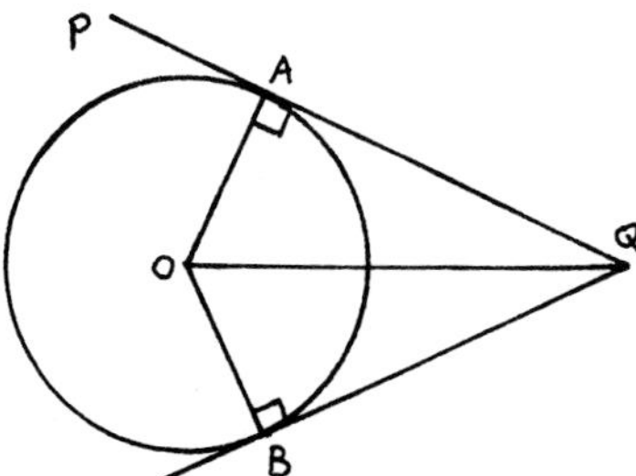

O is the centre; PAQ and RBQ are tangents.

(1) $O\hat{A}P = O\hat{A}Q = O\hat{B}R = O\hat{B}Q = 90°$
(2) OA = OB
(3) AQ = BQ
(4) $A\hat{O}Q = B\hat{O}Q$ and $A\hat{Q}O = B\hat{Q}O$
(5) OQ bisects $A\hat{O}B$ and $A\hat{Q}B$
(6) ΔAOQ and ΔBOQ are congruent
(7) AQBO is a kite
(8) AB cuts OQ at right angles
(9) OQ bisects AB

REMEMBER (1) All radii of the same circle are of equal length (2) The letter O in a circle diagram always means the centre.

a Find the sizes of angles a, b, c, d, e, f, g, h, i, j.

b Find the sizes of angles k, l, m, n, p. AB, CD, EF, GH and IJ are straight lines.

c Find the sizes of angles q, r, s, t, u, v, w, x, y, z.

d Find the sizes of angles a, b, c, d, e, f, g, h, i, j.

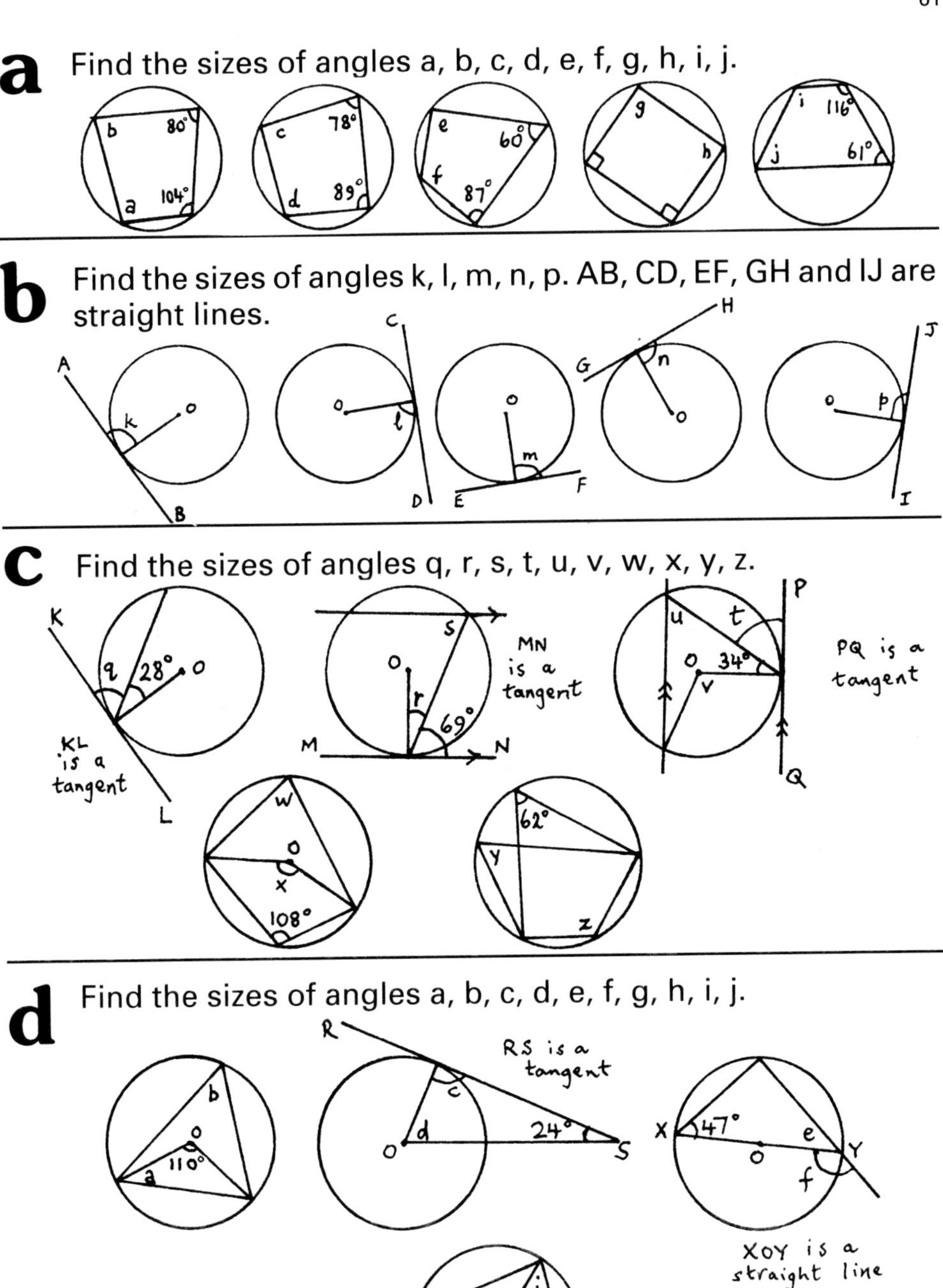

'ANGLE CHASING' WITH CIRCLES

Some rules to remember

1) All radii of the same circle are equal in length.
2) Angles in the same segment are equal.
3) Angle in a semicircle is 90°.
4) Angle at the centre is twice the angle at the circumference.
5) Opposite angles of a cyclic quadrilateral are supplementary (add up to 180°)
6) Tangent is at right angles to the radius where it touches the circle.

It is a good idea also to revise other angle rules (see Maths for Practice & Revision, Book 4, page 66)

---

e.g. In this circle, find (i) $D\hat{A}B$, (ii) $O\hat{A}B$, (iii) $D\hat{A}O$, (iv) $A\hat{O}E$, (v) $E\hat{F}A$, (vi) $O\hat{E}F$, (vii) $C\hat{A}F$, (viii) $D\hat{E}F$, giving brief reasons for your answers.

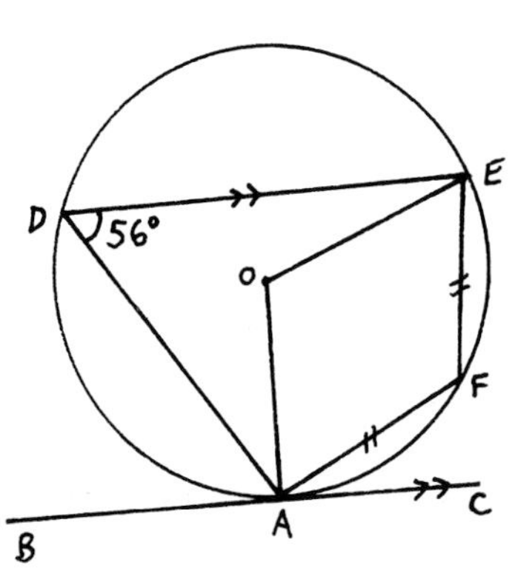

(i) $D\hat{A}B = 56°$ (alternate with $A\hat{D}E$)

(ii) $O\hat{A}B = 90°$ (angle between tangent AB and radius OA)

(iii) $D\hat{A}O = 34°$ ($O\hat{A}B$ subtract $D\hat{A}B$)

(iv) $A\hat{O}E = 112°$ (angle at centre is twice angle $A\hat{D}E$)

(v) $E\hat{F}A = 124°$ (opposite to $A\hat{D}E$ in cyclic quad ADEF = 180°)

(vi) $O\hat{E}F = 62°$ (OEFA is a kite with $O\hat{E}F = O\hat{A}F$. Angles in a quadrilateral = 360°)

(vii) $C\hat{A}F = 28°$ ($O\hat{A}C = 90°$, angle between tangent BAC and radius OA)

(viii) $D\hat{E}F = 84°$ (opposite to $D\hat{A}F$ in cyclic quadrilateral ADEF, and $D\hat{A}F = D\hat{A}O + O\hat{A}F = 34° + 62° = 96°$)

IF IN DIFFICULTY, fill in **ANY** angles which you can work out. This may help you to find the one you want.

a In each diagram O is the centre of the circle. Give brief reasons for your answers.

1)

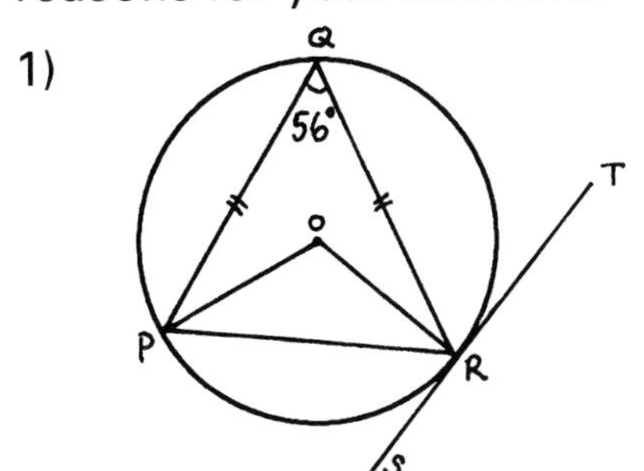

SRT is a straight line.
PQ = RQ
Find $P\hat{O}R$, $O\hat{R}P$, $Q\hat{R}P$, $P\hat{R}S$, $O\hat{R}Q$ and $Q\hat{R}T$.

2)

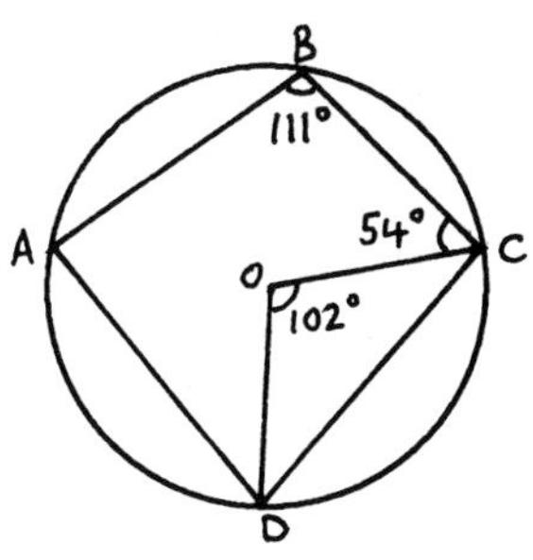

Find $A\hat{D}C$, $O\hat{C}D$, $B\hat{C}D$, $D\hat{A}B$ and $A\hat{D}O$.

3)

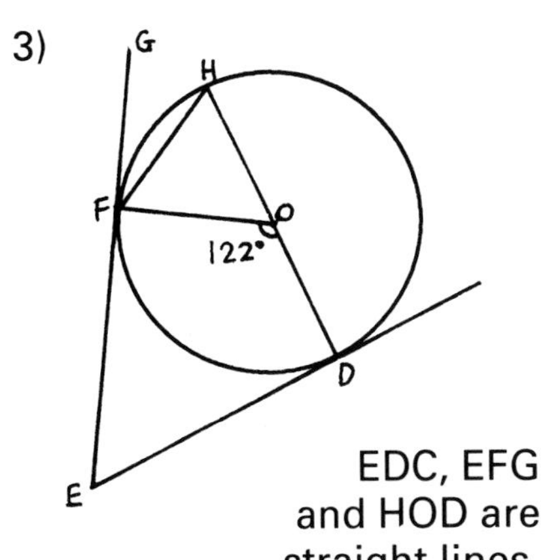

EDC, EFG and HOD are straight lines.
Find $H\hat{O}F$, $D\hat{H}F$, $O\hat{F}E$, $F\hat{E}D$ and $H\hat{F}E$.

4)

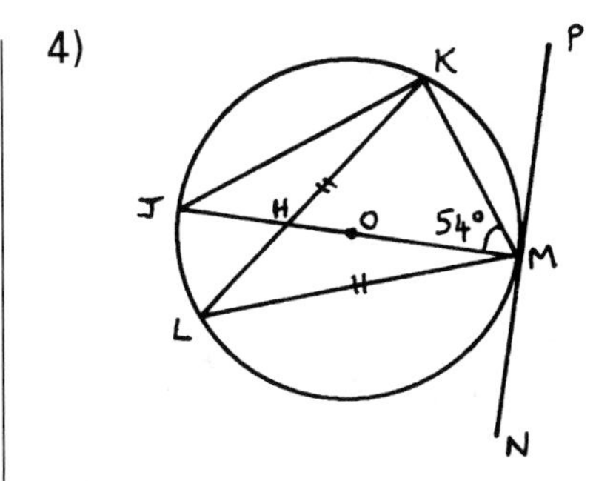

NMP and JOM are straight lines.
Find $J\hat{K}M$, $K\hat{J}M$, $K\hat{L}M$, $K\hat{M}P$, $L\hat{M}K$, $L\hat{M}J$, $L\hat{M}N$, $K\hat{H}M$ and $J\hat{H}L$.

5)

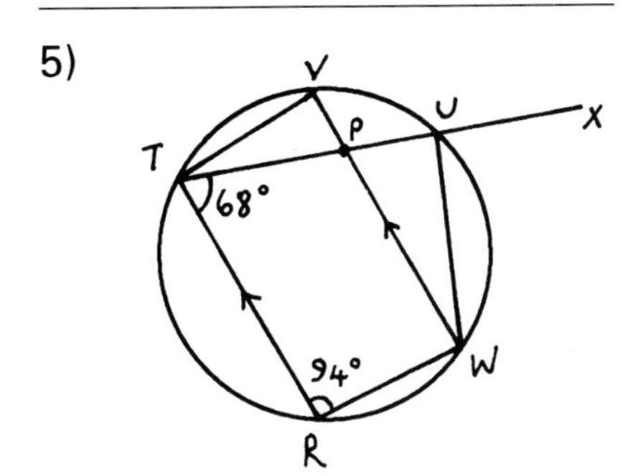

WV and RT are parallel.
$R\hat{T}U = 68°$, $T\hat{R}W = 94°$
Find $T\hat{U}W$, $W\hat{U}X$, $T\hat{V}W$, $T\hat{P}W$ and $P\hat{W}U$.

A SOLID FIGURES (1)

Euler's Formula

The Swiss mathematician Leonhard Euler (pronounced oyler), who lived from 1707 until 1783, found that for many solids the **number of faces** added to the **number of vertices** (corners) was 2 more than the **number of edges,** or

$$\text{faces} + \text{vertices} = \text{edges} + 2$$
$$F + V = E + 2$$

e.g. A cuboid has 6 faces, 8 vertices and 12 edges.

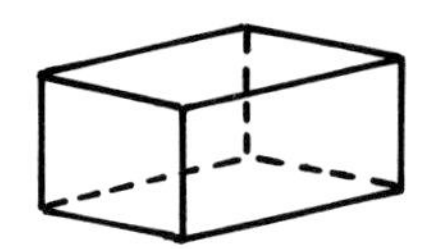

This solid follows Euler's formula.

$$6 + 8 = 12 + 2$$

---

e.g. (2)

A solid made by sticking two congruent (identical) cones base to base has 2 faces, 2 vertices and 1 edge

$$2 + 2 \neq 1 + 2$$

Euler's formula does not apply to this solid.

---

e.g. (3) A solid which follows Euler's formula has 18 faces and 14 vertices. How many edges has it?

$$F + V = E + 2$$
$$18 + 14 = E + 2 \qquad E = 18 + 14 - 2 = 30$$

This solid has 30 edges

Volume of pyramid

Volume of pyramid = $\frac{1}{3}$ X area of base X height

e.g.

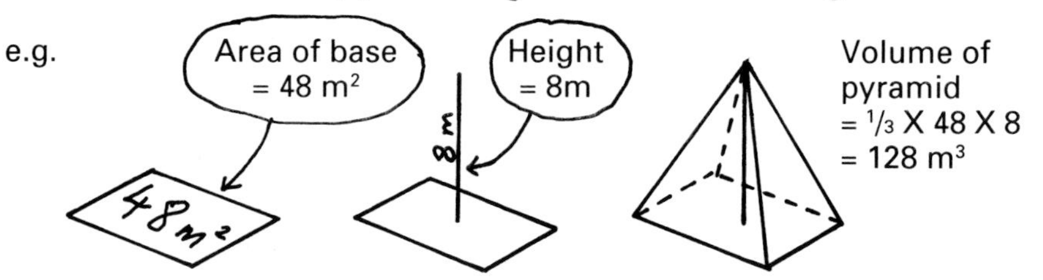

Volume of pyramid
= $\frac{1}{3}$ X 48 X 8
= 128 m^3

NOTE. The height must always be the PERPENDICULAR HEIGHT from the base.

e.g. (2) Find the volume of a pyramid whose height is 10cm and whose base is a square with length 7.2 cm.

Area of base = 7.2 X 7.2 = 51.84 cm^2

Volume of pyramid = $\frac{1}{3}$ X 51.84 X 10 = 172.8 cm^3

REMEMBER. Volume is measured in CUBIC units, e.g. cubic metres (m^3), cubic centimetres (cm^3), etc.

a For each of these solids, list the number of faces, vertices and edges. Write down whether or not Euler's formula applies to the solid.

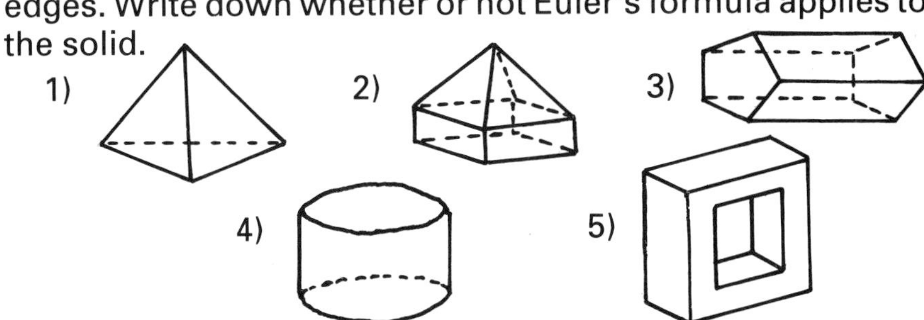

b (All the solids in these questions follow Euler's formula)

1) A solid has 5 faces and 5 vertices. How many edges has it?
2) A dodecahedron has 12 faces and 30 edges. How many vertices has it?
3) A solid has 21 edges and 14 vertices. Calculate the number of faces it has.
4) An octahedron has 8 faces and 6 vertices. Find how many edges it has.
5) (a) A hendecagonal pyramid (whose base is an 11 sided figure) has 12 faces and 12 vertices. How many edges has it?
(b) If two congruent hendecagonal pyramids are stuck base to base to make a new solid, how many (i) faces, (ii) vertices, (iii) edges, has the new solid?

c Find the volumes of these pyramids. The perpendicular height and the area of the base are given for each.

1) Area of base $6m^2$, perpendicular height 2m
2) Area of base $24cm^2$, perpendicular height 7cm
3) Area of base $3m^2$, perpendicular height 1m
4) Area of base $10m^2$, perpendicular height 4.2m
5) Area of base $4x\ cm^2$, perpendicular height $12y$ cm

d Find the volumes of these square pyramids. The perpendicular height and the length of the square base are given for each.

1) Length of base 9cm, perpendicular height 11cm
2) Length of base 0.6m, perpendicular height 0.5m
3) Length of base 2m, perpendicular height 1.5cm
4) Length of base 20cm, perpendicular height 30cm
5) Length of base 13cm, perpendicular height 21cm

A SOLID FIGURES (2)

Cylinders and Cones

A CYLINDER is a prism with a circular base.

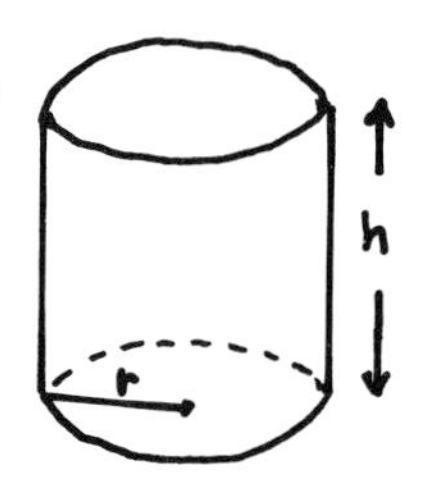

Surface area of cylinder

Area of curved surface of cylinder

r = radius of base

h = height

Area of curved surface = $2\pi rh$

e.g. Find the area of the curved surface of a cylindrical tin which has radius 3cm and height 10cm ($\pi = 3.14$)

$$A = 2 \times 3.14 \times 3 \times 10$$
$$= \underline{188.4 \text{ cm}^2}$$

Total surface area of cylinder

$$= \text{Area of curved surface } (2\pi rh)$$
$$+ \text{ Area of base } (\pi r^2)$$
$$+ \text{ Area of top } (\pi r^2)$$

e.g. Calculate the total surface area of a cylinder with radius 4cm and height 6cm ($\pi = 3.14$).

$$A = (2\pi rh) + (\pi r^2) + (\pi r^2)$$
$$= 2\pi r(h + r)$$
$$= 2 \times 3.14 \times 4 \times 10 = \underline{251.2 \text{ cm}^2}$$

B Volume of cylinder

Volume = $\pi r^2 h$

e.g. What is the volume (V) of a cylinder whose radius is 10cm and whose height is 32cm ($\pi = 3.14$) ?

$$V = 3.14 \times 10 \times 10 \times 32 = \underline{10048 \text{ cm}^3}$$

A CONE is a pyramid with a circular base

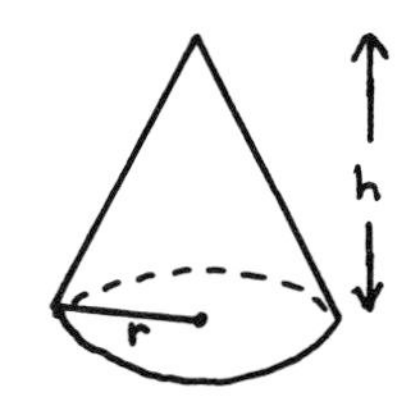

Volume of cone

r = radius

h = height

$$\text{Volume} = \tfrac{1}{3}\pi r^2 h \quad \text{or} \quad \frac{\pi r^2 h}{3}$$

e.g. Find the volume of a cone which is 12cm high and has a radius of 5cm ($\pi = 3.14$).

$$V = \frac{3.14 \times 5 \times 5 \times 12}{3} = \underline{314 \text{ cm}^3}$$

Give answers to 2 significant figures

a ($\pi = 3.14$) Find the area of the curved surface of a cylinder with

1) radius 5cm, height 8cm
2) radius 2cm, height 6cm
3) radius 1m, height 1m
4) radius 6cm, height 20cm
5) radius 3m, height 10m
6) radius 10cm, height 50cm
7) radius $\frac{1}{2}$m, height 2m
8) radius 0.7m, height 1.2m
9) radius 4cm, height 8cm
10) radius 11cm, height 30cm

b ($\pi = 3.14$) Find the total surface area of a cylinder with

1) radius 8cm, height 15cm
2) radius 5cm, height 5cm
3) radius 4cm, height 8cm
4) radius 1m, height 2m
5) radius 6cm, height 9cm

c Find the volume of a cylinder with

($\pi = \frac{22}{7}$)

1) radius 4cm, height 7cm
2) radius 10cm, height 35cm
3) radius 14cm, height 11cm
4) radius $\frac{1}{2}$ m, height $1\frac{2}{5}$ m
5) radius 63cm, height 60cm

($\pi = 3.14$)

6) radius 10cm, height 20cm
7) radius 0.3m, height 1m
8) radius 4cm, height 8cm
9) diameter 18cm, height 18cm
10) radius 6cm, height 50cm

d ($\pi = 3.14$) Find the volume of a cone with

1) radius 6cm, height 6cm
2) radius 3cm, height 10cm
3) radius 0.5m, height 0.8m
4) radius 20cm, height 90cm
5) radius 15cm, height 24cm

e

1) What is the volume of a cylindrical biscuit tin with radius 13cm and height 12 cm?

2) A cylindrical cardboard tube for storing posters has a radius of 4cm and a height of 80cm. Find the area of cardboard used to make the tube (the area of the curved surface).

3) A firework in the shape of a cone has a radius of 5cm and is 10cm high. Find its volume.

4) An unopened cylindrical baked-bean can has a height of 6cm and a radius of 4cm. What is the total surface area?

5) ($\pi = \frac{22}{7}$) A cylindrical bin, radius 28cm and height 60cm, is filled with salt.

(a) What volume of salt does it contain?

(b) The salt is used to fill cylindrical drums of radius 4cm, height 14cm. By first finding the volume of each drum, calculate how many drums can be filled.

SOME EXTRA QUESTIONS ($\pi = 3.14$)

1) (a) Multiply out $(2x + 5)(x + 4)$
   (b) Multiply out $(x - 9)(x + 9)$

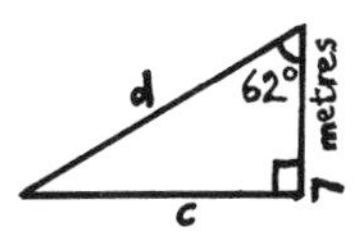

2) Calculate the lengths of c and d (3 sig. figs.)

3) Solve these simultaneous equations $3x - y = 20$, $5x + y = 28$

$$\begin{aligned} 3x - y &= 20 \\ 5x + y &= 28 \end{aligned}$$

4) (a) Find the square root of 3200 (3 sig. figs.)
   (b) Find the value of $\sqrt{0.074}$ (3 sig. figs.)

5) In the winter the owner of a house used 230 units of gas, 2050 units of electricity and 201 telephone units. In the spring he used 175 units of gas, 1640 electricity and 190 telephone. (a) Write these figures as a 3 X 2 matrix F. (b) Unit costs are: gas 40p per unit, electricity 6p, telephone 5p. Write these as a 1 X 3 matrix E. (c) Multiply EF and say what information this answer gives.

6) The longest side of a right-angled triangle is 61 cm long. One of the other sides is 60cm long. What is the length of the third side?

7) Using the table on page 72, or an electronic calculator, find the values of (a) sin 28°, (b) cos 61°, (c) 3 tan 40° (2 dec. places)

8) (i) Find (a) the median, (b) the range of

   60 64 63 68 71 58 67 70 58 73 68 59 69

   (ii) Find the mode in this group of letters

   P, E, A, R, T, R, E, E, C, O, T, T, A, G, E

9) An unopened cylindrical can has radius 6cm, height 17cm. Calculate (a) the area of its curved surface, (b) its total surface area, including top and bottom. (2 sig. figs.)

10) 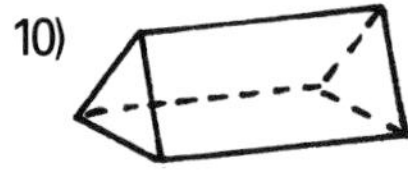

Write out Euler's formula and show how the formula applies to a triangular prism (shown in the diagram)

11) (a) $\begin{pmatrix} 3 & 2 \\ 1 & -2 \end{pmatrix} + \begin{pmatrix} -4 & 5 \\ 2 & -1 \end{pmatrix} + \begin{pmatrix} 2 & -3 \\ 4 & 0 \end{pmatrix}$

   (b) $4\begin{pmatrix} 1 & 2 \\ 0 & 4 \end{pmatrix} - \begin{pmatrix} 4 & -2 \\ 5 & 7 \end{pmatrix}$

12) Find the sizes of angles a and b

13) Add the vectors $\vec{RT}\begin{pmatrix} 3 \\ 2 \end{pmatrix}$ and $\vec{TZ}\begin{pmatrix} -5 \\ 3 \end{pmatrix}$. Write your answer as a column vector $\vec{RZ}$ and draw a diagram to represent the three vectors.

14) (a) Factorise into two brackets $x^2 + 9x + 18$
    (b) Factorise $3x^2 - 18x + 24$

15) (a) Find the circumference of a circle with radius 11cm (2 sig. figs.)
    (b) What is the perimeter of a semicircle with radius 6m (2 sig. figs.)?

16) Solve these quadratic equations by factorising into two brackets
    (i) $x^2 - 10x - 24 = 0$
    (ii) $2x^2 + 7x = 15$

17) 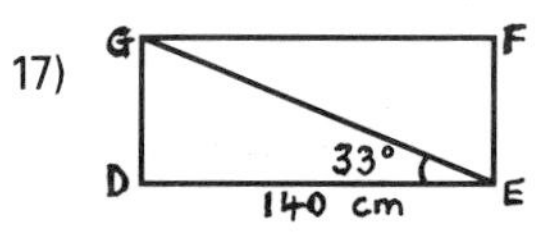

The diagram shows a rectangular table top with DE=140cm and $D\hat{E}G = 33°$.

Calculate, to the nearest centimetre, the perimeter of the table top.

18) Find the values of x and y if $\begin{pmatrix} 8 & x \\ 2y & 3 \end{pmatrix}\begin{pmatrix} 2 \\ 5 \end{pmatrix} = \begin{pmatrix} 6 \\ 11 \end{pmatrix}$

19) Five pencils and two rulers cost £1.03 altogether; three pencils and four rulers cost £1.29 altogether. Working in pence, use simultaneous equations to find the cost of (a) a pencil, (b) a ruler.

20) 20m, 9m, x

Work out the sine of angle x and, from your answer, write down the size of angle x (to the nearest degree).

21) (a) $\begin{pmatrix} 2 & 3 \end{pmatrix}\begin{pmatrix} 5 & 3 \\ 4 & 2 \end{pmatrix}$

(b) $\begin{pmatrix} 1 & 2 \\ 2 & 1 \end{pmatrix}\begin{pmatrix} 7 \\ 6 \end{pmatrix}$

22) Calculate the area of (a) a circle with radius 6.5cm (2 sig. figs.)
(b) a semicircle with diameter 8cm (2 sig. figs.)

23) Find the possible values of x in each equation
(i) $(x-2)(x-5)=0$ (ii) $(2x-4)(x+9)=0$

24) Vector $a = \begin{pmatrix} 2 \\ 1 \end{pmatrix}$, $b = \begin{pmatrix} -3 \\ 2 \end{pmatrix}$. Write as column vectors (i) $4a - b$
(ii) $3b + 2a$

25) (i) Multiply $\begin{pmatrix} 2 \\ 3 \\ 4 \end{pmatrix}\begin{pmatrix} 5 \end{pmatrix}$

(ii) Premultiply $\begin{pmatrix} 1 & 3 & 7 \end{pmatrix}$ by $\begin{pmatrix} 5 \\ 4 \end{pmatrix}$

26) ICE CREAM, SPONGE CAKE

The diagram shows the circular cross-section (looking end on) of a cylindrical ice cream roll made of ice cream surrounded by sponge cake. The outer radius is 3.6cm and the inner radius is 2.8cm. Find (a) the area of sponge cake, (b) the volume of sponge cake if the roll is 11cm long. (2 sig. figs.)

27) (a) Multiply out $3(a+2)(a-3)$
(b) Multiply out $(x-13)^2$

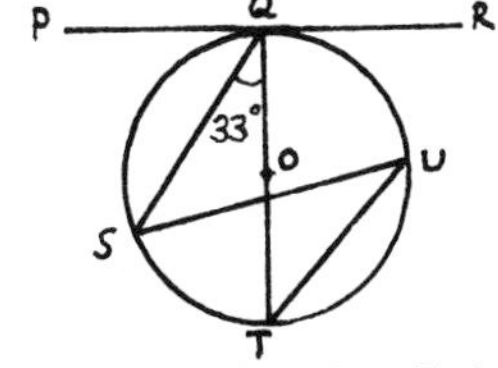

28) Find the size of (i) $R\hat{Q}O$, (ii) $P\hat{Q}S$, (iii) $S\hat{U}T$.
(PQR and QOT are straight lines)

29) To measure the height of the top of St Dominic's church spire, Toby stands 150m away and points his clinometer at the top of the spire. The clinometer records 21°. How high is the top of the spire?

30) Find the values of x and y if $3x + 2y = 18$ and $4x - 5y = 1$

31) Work out (a) the determinant, (b) the inverse of $\begin{pmatrix} 5 & 3 \\ 6 & 4 \end{pmatrix}$

32) Find (a) the mean, (b) the mode, (c) the median of this group of numbers

8 5 6 2 7 1 6 5 3 6
3 1 4 5 9 6 4 3 9 2

33) By using the formula on page 38 C solve this quadratic equation correct to 2 decimal places: $3x^2 - 8x + 2 = 0$

34) (a) On squared paper, plot points (−1, 3), (−1, 5), (−2, 3) and join them to form a triangle. (b) Write the coordinates as a 2 X 3 matrix and premultiply by $\begin{pmatrix} 0 & 1 \\ -1 & 0 \end{pmatrix}$.

(c)Plot the points of the triangle given by the answer to (b) and describe fully what sort of transformation it is.

35) Twelve similar counters numbered ① ② ③ ④ ⑤ ⑥ ⑦ ⑧ ⑨ ⑩ ⑪ ⑫ are put in a bag and mixed up. Find the probability that a counter picked out of the bag will show
(a) an even number, (b) the number 13, (c) a prime number.

36) (i) Factorise $25x^2 - 36$
(ii) Factorise hm − kn − hn + km

37) A certain solid figure which follows Euler's formula has 14 vertices and 9 faces. How many edges has it?

38) The drive of a house is a steady slope of 16 metres from the road up to the front door. The drive makes an angle of 10° with the horizontal. How much higher than the road is the front door? Give answer to 2 significant figures.

39) Vector $a=\begin{pmatrix}-1\\1\end{pmatrix}$, $b=\begin{pmatrix}3\\2\end{pmatrix}$. $\overrightarrow{OK} = 3a$, $\overrightarrow{ON} = 2b$. (i) Draw $\overrightarrow{OK}$, $\overrightarrow{ON}$ and $\overrightarrow{NK}$. (ii) Write $\overrightarrow{NK}$ as a column vector and also in terms of a and b.

40) By drawing graphs, solve the simultaneous equations
$y = 3x - 2$ and $y = \frac{1}{2}x + 3$

41) Find the volume of (a) a pyramid with height 14cm and area of base 144 cm^2 (b) a cone with height 9cm and radius 4cm. (2 sig. figs.)

42) Multiply these matrices $\begin{pmatrix}5 & 3\\1 & -2\end{pmatrix}\begin{pmatrix}0 & 1 & -2\\-1 & 3 & 4\end{pmatrix}$

43) There are 9 blue buttons, 6 red buttons and 21 white buttons in a box. (a) If I choose a button without looking, what is the probability that it will be blue? (b) If the button I have chosen is indeed blue and I leave it out of the box, what is the probability of choosing a white button if I dip into the box again?

44) Calculate the magnitude of vector $\begin{pmatrix}-5\\3\end{pmatrix}$. Give your answer to 3 significant figures.

45)
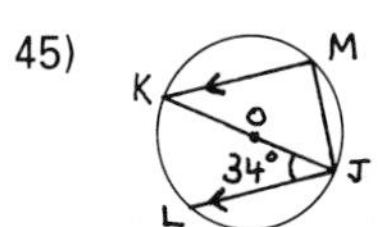

KOJ is a straight line; KM and LJ are parallel.
Find the sizes of (i) $J\hat{K}M$, (ii) $K\hat{M}J$, (iii) $M\hat{J}K$

46) Two boats 'Anna' and 'Billy' are heading for a port. 'Anna' is 2km due west of 'Billy' and 'Billy' is due south of the port. If 'Anna' sails on a bearing of 033° how far must she go to reach the port (2 sig. figs.)?

47) (a) Write these simultaneous equations in matrix form, and
(b) solve for x and y
$4x + 3y = 1$
$x + 2y = 4$

48) Sally is flying a kite on a string 240m long. The string makes an angle of 63° with the ground. What is the vertical height of the kite above the ground? (2 sig. figs.)

49) Clare told Adrian she had thought of a number, squared it, and then added the original number, making the final answer 30. Adrian guessed she had thought of 5 but he was wrong. What was Clare's original number?

50) A = 1, B = 2, C = 3, D = 4, E = 5, F = 6, G = 7. Carol uses the matrix

$\begin{pmatrix}2 & -3\\-3 & 5\end{pmatrix}$ to decode the message $\begin{pmatrix}25 & 26 & 41\\16 & 17 & 26\end{pmatrix}$. What was the original

message?

SQUARE ROOTS

SQUARE ROOTS OF NUMBERS from 1.0 to 10.0 (3 sig. figs.)			
Number n	*Square Root* $\sqrt{n}$	*Number* n	*Square Root* $\sqrt{n}$
		5.1	2.26
		5.2	2.28
		5.3	2.30
		5.4	2.32
		5.5	2.35
		5.6	2.37
		5.7	2.39
		5.8	2.41
		5.9	2.43
1.0	**1.00**	6.0	2.45
1.1	1.05	6.1	2.47
1.2	1.10	6.2	2.49
1.3	1.14	6.3	2.51
1.4	1.18	6.4	2.53
1.5	1.22	6.5	2.55
1.6	1.26	6.6	2.57
1.7	1.30	6.7	2.59
1.8	1.34	6.8	2.61
1.9	1.38	6.9	2.63
2.0	1.41	7.0	2.65
2.1	1.45	7.1	2.66
2.2	1.48	7.2	2.68
2.3	1.52	7.3	2.70
2.4	1.55	7.4	2.72
2.5	1.58	7.5	2.74
2.6	1.61	7.6	2.76
2.7	1.64	7.7	2.77
2.8	1.67	7.8	2.79
2.9	1.70	7.9	2.81
3.0	1.73	8.0	2.83
3.1	1.76	8.1	2.85
3.2	1.79	8.2	2.86
3.3	1.82	8.3	2.88
3.4	1.84	8.4	2.90
3.5	1.87	8.5	2.92
3.6	1.90	8.6	2.93
3.7	1.92	8.7	2.95
3.8	1.95	8.8	2.97
3.9	1.97	8.9	2.98
4.0	**2.00**	**9.0**	**3.00**
4.1	2.02	9.1	3.02
4.2	2.05	9.2	3.03
4.3	2.07	9.3	3.05
4.4	2.10	9.4	3.07
4.5	2.12	9.5	3.08
4.6	2.14	9.6	3.10
4.7	2.17	9.7	3.11
4.8	2.19	9.8	3.13
4.9	2.21	9.9	3.15
5.0	2.24	10.0	3.16

SQUARE ROOTS OF NUMBERS from 10 to 100 (3 sig. figs.)			
Number n	*Square Root* $\sqrt{n}$	*Number* n	*Square Root* $\sqrt{n}$
		51	7.14
		52	7.21
		53	7.28
		54	7.35
		55	7.42
		56	7.48
		57	7.55
		58	7.62
		59	7.68
10	3.16	60	7.75
11	3.32	61	7.81
12	3.46	62	7.87
13	3.61	63	7.94
14	3.74	**64**	**8.00**
15	3.87	65	8.06
16	**4.00**	66	8.12
17	4.12	67	8.19
18	4.24	68	8.25
19	4.36	69	8.31
20	4.47	70	8.37
21	4.58	71	8.43
22	4.69	72	8.49
23	4.80	73	8.54
24	4.90	74	8.60
25	**5.00**	75	8.66
26	5.10	76	8.72
27	5.20	77	8.77
28	5.29	78	8.83
29	5.39	79	8.89
30	5.48	80	8.94
31	5.57	**81**	**9.00**
32	5.66	82	9.06
33	5.74	83	9.11
34	5.83	84	9.17
35	5.92	85	9.22
36	**6.00**	86	9.27
37	6.08	87	9.33
38	6.16	88	9.38
39	6.24	89	9.43
40	6.32	90	9.49
41	6.40	91	9.54
42	6.48	92	9.59
43	6.56	93	9.64
44	6.63	94	9.70
45	6.71	95	9.75
46	6.78	96	9.80
47	6.86	97	9.85
48	6.93	98	9.90
49	**7.00**	99	9.95
50	7.07	**100**	**10.0**

PERFECT SQUARES are numbers whose square roots are exact integers (whole numbers). Perfect squares and their square roots are shown in **BOLD PRINT.**

SINES, COSINES AND TANGENTS (correct to 2 decimal places)

ANGLE degrees	*sin*	*cos*	*tan*
00	0	1.00	0
01	0.02	1.00	0.02
02	0.03	1.00	0.03
03	0.05	1.00	0.05
04	0.07	1.00	0.07
05	0.09	1.00	0.09
06	0.10	1.00	0.11
07	0.12	0.99	0.12
08	0.14	0.99	0.14
09	0.16	0.99	0.16
10	0.17	0.98	0.18
11	0.19	0.98	0.19
12	0.21	0.98	0.21
13	0.22	0.97	0.23
14	0.24	0.97	0.25
15	0.26	0.97	0.27
16	0.28	0.96	0.29
17	0.29	0.96	0.31
18	0.31	0.95	0.32
19	0.33	0.95	0.34
20	0.34	0.94	0.36
21	0.36	0.93	0.38
22	0.37	0.93	0.40
23	0.39	0.92	0.42
24	0.41	0.91	0.45
25	0.42	0.91	0.47
26	0.44	0.90	0.49
27	0.45	0.89	0.51
28	0.47	0.88	0.53
29	0.48	0.87	0.55
30	0.50	0.87	0.58
31	0.52	0.86	0.60
32	0.53	0.85	0.62
33	0.54	0.84	0.65
34	0.56	0.83	0.67
35	0.57	0.82	0.70
36	0.59	0.81	0.73
37	0.60	0.80	0.75
38	0.62	0.79	0.78
39	0.63	0.78	0.81
40	0.64	0.77	0.84
41	0.66	0.75	0.87
42	0.67	0.74	0.90
43	0.68	0.73	0.93
44	0.69	0.72	0.97
45	0.71	0.71	1.00

ANGLE degrees	*sin*	*cos*	*tan*
46	0.72	0.69	1.04
47	0.73	0.68	1.07
48	0.74	0.67	1.11
49	0.75	0.66	1.15
50	0.77	0.64	1.19
51	0.78	0.63	1.23
52	0.79	0.62	1.28
53	0.80	0.60	1.33
54	0.81	0.59	1.38
55	0.82	0.57	1.43
56	0.83	0.56	1.48
57	0.84	0.54	1.54
58	0.85	0.53	1.60
59	0.86	0.52	1.66
60	0.87	0.50	1.73
61	0.87	0.48	1.80
62	0.88	0.47	1.88
63	0.89	0.45	1.96
64	0.90	0.44	2.05
65	0.91	0.42	2.14
66	0.91	0.41	2.25
67	0.92	0.39	2.36
68	0.93	0.37	2.48
69	0.93	0.36	2.61
70	0.94	0.34	2.75
71	0.95	0.33	2.90
72	0.95	0.31	3.08
73	0.96	0.29	3.27
74	0.96	0.28	3.49
75	0.97	0.26	3.73
76	0.97	0.24	4.01
77	0.97	0.22	4.33
78	0.98	0.21	4.70
79	0.98	0.19	5.14
80	0.98	0.17	5.67
81	0.99	0.16	6.31
82	0.99	0.14	7.12
83	0.99	0.12	8.14
84	0.99	0.10	9.51
85	1.00	0.09	11.43
86	1.00	0.07	14.30
87	1.00	0.05	19.08
88	1.00	0.03	28.64
89	1.00	0.02	57.29
90	1.00	0	∞

∞ means 'infinity' (the highest imaginable number)